THE COMPLETE WEBSITE PLANNING GUIDE WORKBOOK

Step-by-step exercises to help you plan and create the briefing document
for your next website project.

DARRYL KING

ireckon™
publishing

Published by Ireckon Pty Ltd

Requests to publish work from this book should be sent to publishing@ireckon.com

National Library of Australia Cataloguing-in-Publication entry : (paperback)

Creator: King, Darryl, author,

Title: The complete website planning guide workbook : Step-by-step exercises to help you plan and create the briefing document for your next website project / Darryl King

ISBN: 978-0-6480537-2-9

Subjects: Website development-Handbooks, manuals, etc.

Web sites-- Authoring programs

Web sites-- Design.

Web publishing.

Table of Contents

INTRODUCTION   **1**
How To Use This Workbook   3
No Existing Website   3

GOALS   **6**
What Results Do You Want From Your Website?   7
Additional Goals   13
Goal Sheet   17

AUDIENCE   **18**
Planning Your Site Around The People Who Will Use It.   19
Understanding Your Existing Audience   21
Who Are They?   28
What's Their Problem?   32
Customer Snapshot Example   36
Digging Deeper   41
What Problems Are You Currently Solving?   43
What Do You Want To Provide?   44
What Problem Do These Products Solve?   45
Understanding Your Customer's Problems   52
Understanding Problems   53
Spotting the Gaps   63
Personas   70
Sample Persona   71

MUST HAVES   **82**
What Must Your Business Have?   83

RESEARCH   **88**
Researching Your Market   89
Gathering Information   90
Content Performance   91
Most Visited Pages   92
Top Landing Pages   93
Lowest Bounce Rate   95
Highest Bounce Rate   97
Top Pages From Search   99

Most Important Pathway Pages   101

Demographic Information   103

Device Information   104

Additional Data   105

User Behavior Observations   117

SORTING THE DATA   126
Time to Sort the Data   127

Affinity Diagram   128

Example Affinity Diagram   130

Sorting the Data   131

Finalizing Your Research.   135

SITEMAPPING   140
Sitemap Your Website   141

What Does a Sitemap Look Like?   144

Sitemap Example 1   144

About Example 1   145

Sitemap Example 2   146

About Example 2   147

Starting Your Sitemap   148

Next Steps   149

Completing the Sitemap   150

SCOPING   158
The Website Scope   159

Scope Template   161

Filling In The Template   162

WIREFRAMING   168
Wireframe Your Pages   169

Wirefame For Devices   171

Key Components of Wireframing   172

Mobile First   174

Where to Start   175

From Scope to Wireframe   176

Wireframe Every Page   179

Wireframe the Home Page   180

Wireframe Templates   181

CONTENT   192
Planning Your Content   193

Scoping Page Content   194

Get Specific   195

Content Requirements Document List   196

List Explanation   197

THE FINAL DOCUMENT   **198**

Completing Your Website Brief   199

Your Finished Brief   200

What's Next?   204

A Note From Darryl   207

About The Author   208

Acknowledgements   208

Also By Darryl King   209

➤ Introduction

In my first book **The Complete Website Planning Guide** I posed several questions about the desire to have more control over your website projects, how to get the best out of them and where to start when preparing a brief.

I have been humbled by how well the book has sold and been received, and that it has been able to help so many people with their web projects.

I have been asked for specific examples and further information on parts of my process and so this workbook became a way to explain in more detail how we do what we do in a practical and useable format.

Expanding on the step-by-step process I outlined in the original book, this workbook includes individual exercises and instruction for each of the steps needed to create a quality scope of works for your next web project.

We have allowed a lot of working space within this workbook so you can write or draw as you work through it. We have also linked to downloadable templates in case you run out of room.

Given the expanded nature of this book, there are elements within it which are additional to the original book, such as the scoping information on functional elements. I have also increased the amount of depth on each step, challenging you to think in more depth about the work you are doing, especially within the research sections.

While I touched on the research part of scoping a website in the original book, it is an area that is often skipped over because of the effort it requires. I would like to challenge you to not only follow my prompts in this workbook but to find additional resources that will help you in this area. The more research you are prepared to do the better results you will create for your project.

Who is this workbook for?

This workbook is intended as a companion to the original book but can also be used on its own to create a complete website brief.

Like the original it has multiple audiences.

Business owners and marketing teams can use it to create the brief for the internal teams or to help them choose the right development partner.

Agency teams can use it as a resource to provide to their customers as a way to help them prepare their briefs as much as it will highlight their involvement in the process. It is still my belief that the site owners need to take as much responsibility over the brief as possible. It is their business, after all.

Freelancers and developers should be making sure the clients they work with give them better briefs. Use it as a resource to guide scoping, get your clients to fill it in or use it to workshop with your clients. It can, as it has for me, open up new service options for you to charge your clients to do workshops, partial or full briefing with them.

When there is a quality brief outlining the requirements the projects will run better, that I can guarantee.

More importantly if you commit to this level of work for your projects, the end results will always be better.

This process doesn't rely on any individual's expertise to make a project better; it provides a way to ensure that each and every project runs better.

Students and teachers can use this workbook to learn the right ways to plan and scope websites before any drawing or coding is started.

Why is this guide needed?

In an era where websites and apps are the norm in everyday life we still find many sites underperform. They don't live up to the expectations of the companies that invest in them.

There is no shortage of design and development talent around the world, the tools to make a website are cheaper and easier to use than ever before.

Yet many client side executives will complain about the way their web assets work, or more importantly don't, and the frustration they have in getting something built to work.

The Complete Website Planning Guide and **Workbook** were designed to provide a step-by-step process that creates the documents outlining the exact requirements, using a thoughtful and research based model.

On the developer side many projects can cost the developer or agency money and time that wasn't budgeted for, simply because not enough information was exposed early on in the process.

It is in everyone's best interest to prepare better briefs.

Follow the processes set out in this workbook, and you will be ahead of your competitors from the beginning!

If you care about your website, then this workbook will help you plan, build and get better results from it.

The workbook is set out in the same order as the original book, however the chapter headings are task focused for the area you are working on.

E.g. Goals or Audience.

They relate to the same chapters in the original book such as 'What's the result you want?' or 'Who's your audience?'

Each section has instructions, examples and areas for you to complete the work.

In some areas it is in minute detail while in others you need to gather the information and lay it into the worksheets.

Whether you use a pen, pencil, post-it notes or anything else doesn't matter. What matters is that you complete each of the exercises and in doing so uncover the information that will help you rethink how a website should be built and then what website will work best for you.

If I help you change the way you approach your websites and not just do what everyone else does, then I will have succeeded in the reason for this workbook.

How To Use This Workbook

The workbook contains extended information about the processes you can use to build your website plan.

Where the original **Complete Website Planning Guide** talks through all of the concepts and explains the steps to creating your plan, this workbook offers exercises and expanded detail on how to do it.

In the research areas, the original book spoke at a macro level on what was required and pointed to methods you could use for your research.

In this workbook, we provide sections to write down the research, analyze it and suggestions for your work.

We have used formulas, examples and step-by-step processes with space to write down your responses.

There are templates for all of the steps in **The Complete Website Planning Guide** process and also additional free downloads you can use.

The chapters are laid out in a logical sequence, and my suggestion is to work in the order provided. You might like to scan over the workbook quickly on your first read to get a sense of the steps ahead then go back to the beginning and start on the exercises.

Some of the steps take a lot of time and require you to do things you might not be familiar with. I implore you to do the work, and you will earn the benefits.

The paper used in this workbook is perfect for writing into, drawing on and making many notes. Fill in the book with your notes and sketches. Good luck with your website planning.

No Existing Website

Is your business new and you don't have an existing site, or you just don't have an existing website? No problem.

Initially, when I drafted this workbook, I included additional explanations in some areas for people who are embarking on a brand new concept.

What happened was that many sections became cumbersome to read, and I realised that that was not the ideal approach.

This section is for you, the person who wants to scope a brand new site without any history. Most likely, this will be a new business venture. If you do have existing customers but no website then you will be more informed, but the explanations below will help you use this workbook.

Many of the core processes aren't affected by whether you have an existing site or not. E.g. Sitemapping and Wireframing.

There are some parts of the process, though that is different or which would be impossible to complete without some additional context. In this chapter, I outline how to approach these parts of the book.

I would suggest you read this chapter thoroughly, then review each section of the workbook so that you can prepare questions for your research. When conducting surveys, you won't get a second chance to go back and get additional answers.

Goals

The setting of goals for your new site should be no different than for anyone else. You will use zero for the current number when working through the formulas.

When setting specific numbers, try not to use blue-sky numbers, but something which you feel accurately reflects what will happen in the early stages of your new site. You will be speculating but having a goal is much better than not.

Audience

The audience section of the workbook has existing customers as its focus. There are several ways you can approach this:

1. Look for competitive or industry analysis. e.g. are there statistics that profile customers across your industry?

2. By conducting market research.

If you can get your hands on industry research, you will be able to fill in some of the fixed lists in the early portion of the Audience chapter.

For some businesses, it is easy to see who their customers are so that you can do competitive analysis. The cheekier amongst you will seek to interview your competitors' customers and ask them pertinent questions from the information in this workbook.

The additional lists in this chapter allow you to record information you can discover from market researching potential customers.

To do this, you will be surveying people who are interested in the product or service you are going to offer. What you need to add into your questions are specifics around how they would expect to see your offer presented online.

You can ask about what they find useful and wrong from other providers, what frustrations they typically experience, and what expectations from you they have.

Where existing businesses should be using only factual information, you will need to use your imagination to extrapolate what you learn from your surveys.

Who Are They?

In this section and the following sections, you will be working through the process of creating your 'fictional' personas. Create names for people based on the surveying you have done and work through building out their profiles as you would with real people's data.

If you have conducted enough face to face, phone or email interviews, you should have plenty of data to use to fill in much of this section. You will still need to use your imagination a little. The exercises in this book will help you to consider how much you do or don't know about the audience you want to target.

It might highlight you need to do more market research.

What Do You Want To Provide?

This section should be about the products or services you have decided you will be bringing to market.

Problem Solving

Again this should be considered for what you are bringing to market. If you haven't already thought about the problems you are solving, then you should be doing that here.

Understanding Problems

This section will require you to have asked questions when you conduct your surveys.

Personas

Complete the personas as you would for your prospective customers, that you should already have identified when planning your new venture.

User Research

There is little you can do without a site to view how existing users use your website. A possible multi-step approach you can consider using is to have your wireframes designed then tested.

In that instance, you would work through as much of the planning process as you can, then work up a series of wireframes. Once you have the wireframes, you have them put into a working prototype which users can work through.

Using online user testing services, you can get test feedback from how users would attempt to use the site.

If you don't want to go that extreme, then you would skip over the section that details out how users use the site.

Observations

You will have enough insight and data collected from the above approaches to complete this section and the rest of the process. The rest of the book works the same for any business or organization.

Start Planning

While you will need to use your imagination in some areas, the process in this workbook will work as well for you as for an existing business.

You're speculating on a new business venture, and that requires imagination and the ability to review and understand the market. Use those skills to help you plan your website.

GOALS

➤ What Results Do You Want From Your Website?

Setting goals for a website is one of the most important parts of any planning project. It's one of the first sections of my original book and this workbook for a very good reason.

The goal or goals of the site dictate priorities and areas of focus, and enable accurate measurement of whether you are getting closer to reaching those goals or not. Like any part of a business, goals force you to make the correct decisions required to achieve them.

Websites typically serve several masters in a business, each with their own objectives. These masters, whether departments, owners, or key people each have their own business goals they are striving to achieve. While each area of an organization is ultimately trying to further the goals of the overall business often they can inadvertently compete with each other.

There needs to be a roadmap that helps guide priorities when you are making design and functionality decisions. Setting goals at the start of your planning project helps you to provide such a roadmap for everyone involved.

> *Setting goals is the first step in turning*
>
> *the invisible into the visible*

The first step in creating your goals is to write out all of the things you believe need improving on your website. Seek suggestions from everyone that has a stake in your site and create a list of anything that comes up.

Don't worry about 'getting it right'; just write out all the things you want to change or believe need to change.

For example: Speed, number of enquires or usability

_____   _____

_____   _____

_____   _____

_____   _____

_____   _____

_____   _____

_____   _____

_____   _____

The list you just completed should be an unfiltered brain dump of all the things that you or others in your organization have mentioned that they want to improve on your site.

Let's now split this list into two groups;

1. Easily Measured. For example visitors, logins, subscribers where you can get real data.

2. Not Easily Measured or Aesthetic. For example a modern look, better navigation etc. where the measurement is subjective.

Copy the items from your previous list into one of the relevant panels below. You might come up with others as you go through this process, so add them at the same time into the panel that suits them best.

Easily Measured

_____

_____

_____

_____

_____

_____

_____

_____

_____

Not Easily Measured/Aesthetic

_____

_____

_____

_____

_____

_____

_____

_____

_____

Now that you have finished copying all of the items into the two columns on the previous page, you need to spend some time with the list of "Easily Measured" items.

Review each one of these with the goal of determining which one would be the most important item to focus on.

Imagine that you can only pick one item to work with, and that you can't use any of the others. In that circumstance which one would be the single individual thing that you would choose to change about your online business?

This choice will become the basis of the Primary Goal for your website.

The Primary Goal for any website is the single most important goal that is more important than any other. E.g. your site might want to increase sales as the Primary Goal, being more important than a lesser goal of newsletter signups.

While other goals will have importance to the business and have their place in a well functioning site, the Primary Goal is the one that the project is likely to be assessed on.

During the project lifecycle different stakeholders in your organization will wish to have their needs met, and will set goals or actions they need to happen on the site.

There will be parts of the site that cannot support having multiple actions happening at once or where it isn't in the best interest of the business overall. There needs to be a method to determine which item will get priority over others.

We use the site hierarchies of the site goals as that method. When a decision needs to be made that has competing interests the goals will become the objective decision makers that allow everyone to understand why the decision is being made.

Example Goal Types:

- Increase inquiries
- More sales
- More time reading our articles

When you have made the choice from the Easily Measured list, record it in the space below as your Primary Goal Type.

Your Primary Goal type is: _____

Now in order to fully define your goal you need to make it measurable, specific and realistic.

Having chosen from the easily measured group we know that this goal can be measured. Now we want to make it specific and also make sure it is realistic.

Setting goals that aren't realistic doesn't help you achieve them. While you need stretch goals that force you into developing ways to reach them, if they are so much of a stretch that no one believes they are achievable they won't help you.

The goal you want to set is one that you have a probability of achieving and one that you and your team can get excited about achieving. It should have a significant impact on your business and as such be worth committing to achieving.

Firstly you need to understand what level you are at now.

If you chose a goal type like "Number of Inquiries" then you need to identify what the current number of inquiries is today.

Realistic goals begin by knowing where we are now so that we can review whether our goal is going to be achievable.

What is the number of the chosen goal type that you currently achieve?

Current Level:

Goal type e.g. Inquiry	A Quantity: How many	per	Period: e.g. month

for example: web inquiries | 10 | per | month

With this number defined we can look to create a stretch goal that is achievable. There is nothing more deflating that realizing part way through a project that you'll never be able to meet the goals. Goals should stretch us but they need to be attainable.

Your Target

Write down the number of your chosen goal type per period you chose that you want to be making in 12 months' time.

Your Target:

B Quantity: How many	per	Period: e.g. month

*E.g. How many **inquiries** (goal type) per **month** (period) do you want to make in 12 months' time? [B] 30 per month*

So how realistic is this?

The easy way to review it is to break it down into shorter timeframes, so you can see how many you will need to make progressively from the starting point until the end point.

While you wouldn't normally have a straight line from month 1 to month 12, it is still useful to check that you haven't undersold your goal or oversold it.

Let's do some simple calculations.

| 6 Month Target: | $C = B / 2$ | C | | per | |
| 3 Month Target: | $D = C / 2$ | D | | per | |

Look at the number D.

Does it seem realistic that you will be able to make that many within 3 months? Does it seem too many? If so by how much, and what is the reason behind that?

Or does it seem too small?

The point of reviewing it isn't to talk yourself out of the number but more to get you to critically review the likelihood of you being able to achieve that result.

There is a lot more to achieving the goal than simply picking the number. You will need to put into place strategies that will help you achieve this target so you should feel like you are capable.

If it is the number of sales you are going to increase, will it be the number of sales, the size of the average sale, the total monetary value sold or some other number?

Growing sales volume numbers means either improving conversion of the existing traffic you have or growing the traffic you are getting. How well have you done that so far? Would it be better if your goal was to grow the traffic rather than sales? Or do you need to change the number you chose?

Try to understand the resources and improvements you and your team will need to make to achieve this goal. Of course there's nothing stopping you having a big stretch goal and making part of your plans to improve the overall methods needed.

So how realistic is your goal? Do you think it is achievable?

(next page to answer) ▶

Great news, then skip down the page to the section called 'Your Specific PRIMARY Website Goal'.

No?

Then let's redo those numbers so they will work for you.

Let's write in the current level again.

Current Level:

	A	per	
goal type	*Quantity: How many*		*Period: e.g. month*

Your Target

Let's start by modifying that 3-month target you were not happy with, then we'll just multiply it up to the 12-month target.

3 Month Target:	*what seems realistic?*	C	per	
6 Month Target:	D = C * 2	D	per	
12 Month Target:	E = D * 2	E	per	

Make sure the numbers above make sense for you and your business. A stretch goal should make you feel uncomfortable, push you out of any comfort zone your business is currently in and require you to think about how you will make this happen but it shouldn't feel like a lottery draw where you just hope it could be that number.

Your Specific Primary Website Goal:

_____

_____   ✓ Specific

_____   ✓ Measurable

✓ Realistic

E.g. e.g. We will be generating 34 web inquiries per month from our website within 12 months (May 12, 20xx).

Or: We will be making an average sale on our site of $134 within 6 months (July 1, 20xx).

Additional Goals

It would be rare if your site has only a single goal. The role of websites and applications touches many parts of an organization and its customers so there are normally several items that you are likely to want to improve.

Your Primary Goal was the most important goal.

Now you should revisit the list of easily measured changes you created at the beginning of this chapter and decide if there are any others of them you want to put as goals for the site.

List those here:

Review your Primary Goal and think about the things that will need to happen to help you achieve that goal. If you need more traffic should you have a traffic goal? If the items are already in the list above don't repeat them, but if not add them to this list.

_____

_____

_____

_____

_____

_____

Now from these two lists you should choose which is the second most important goal for the website, and third. You can have as many goals as you feel work for your organization, however I would caution to limit them to those you will actually measure and that will have an impact on your business.

Work through the same exercises you did earlier for each additional goal.

Remember each goal needs to be specific, realistic and something you can measure.

Secondary Goal

Current Level:

_____   A [   ]   per [   ]
goal type   *Quantity: How many*   *Period: e.g. month*

Your Target

3 Month Target: *what seems realistic?*   C [   ]   per [   ]

6 Month Target: $D = C * 2$ D [   ]   per [   ]

12 Month Target: $E = D * 2$ E [   ]   per [   ]

Now write that secondary goal out below making sure you are specific and it is measurable. If you can't measure it and it isn't speecific then its not the right type of goal to be driving key decisions from.

Your Specific Secondary Website Goal:

_____ ✓ Specific

_____ ✓ Measurable

_____ ✓ Realistic

E.g. we will be generating 34 web inquiries from our website within 12 months of launching (May 12, 2xxx).

Tertiary Goal

Current Level:

_____ A [   ] per [   ]
goal type   *Quantity: How many*   *Period: e.g. month*

Your Target

3 Month Target:	*what seems realistic?*	C [ ]	per	[ ]
6 Month Target:	D = C * 2	D [ ]	per	[ ]
12 Month Target:	E = D * 2	E [ ]	per	[ ]

Your Specific Tertiary Website Goal:

_____

_____

_____

✓ Specific

✓ Measurable

✓ Realistic

E.g. we will be generating 34 web inquiries from our website within 12 months of launching (May 12, 2xxx).

If you need more goal sheets you can download a goals template here: **https://ireck.in/wpgwork**

The exercises you have completed should have helped you get clarity about what this web project is all about.

Goals are the destination for the whole website plan. Like any map, having a destination helps you choose the best routes to use to reach it. Even if you hit roadblocks, knowing your end goal helps you choose alternative strategies without getting distracted.

The goals you have just set should be considered post-it notes that anyone working in the project places on each task they have to do. How will this help achieve these goals, which goal needs priority in this area?

Whether they are making decisions about functionality, design, content etc. they should be considering how to further these goals.

Keep them handy throughout the project.

How to use your website goals?

The goals should be used in conjunction with decisions about layout, design, functionality, content, in fact they are the single most important driver of all decisions and end results of the project.

Nothing on the site should exist without a reason, and ultimately should be related to how it fulfills a goal.

➤ Goal Sheet

Use this page to record each of the three top goals for your website project. Copy them from the previous pages and make sure they are easy to refer back to, keeping in mind that the point of these goals isn't just for the scoping project but for measuring the effectiveness of the site once it is built and working.

Your Primary Website Goal:

_____

_____

_____

Your Secondary Website Goal:

_____

_____

_____

Your Tertiary Website Goal:

_____

_____

_____

AUDIENCE

Planning Your Site Around The People Who Will Use It.

In the previous chapter we focused on setting the goals for your web application. These are your goals and what your organization wants and needs from the site.

These goals will drive many of the decisions you make about the site and how it will work. They help you in decision-making steps later in in the planning and build process.

One flaw of many websites is that while they have a clear set of objectives for their site they let these dictate everything about the site. In doing this they make the website too internally focused, (what's in it for us?), rather than being externally focused.

The purpose of your site is to provide information or value to external people and in doing so to seek to achieve the goals you have for your organization.

How well you do this will dictate how well you achieve your goals.

To achieve your goals you will need to have people using your site. Not just anybody either you will need the right people.

Who are the right people?

This is the question that you will answer during this chapter. We refer to them as your audience. This term is used deliberately over other terms like users or customers.

> Audience
>
> noun [C]
>
> [+ sing/pl verb]
>
> the (number of) people watching or listening to a particular television or radio program, reading a particular book, or visiting a particular website:

At the top level your audience is those people visiting your website. This alone is too superficial and you will need to understand them in a more detailed sense.

The role your website needs to play in relation to your audience is:

- To first help define who that audience is
- To create pathways that will help attract them to the site
- To answer the questions the audience has in relation to your offer
- To assist them in segmenting themselves into the types of audience they are; general searches, researches, possible clients, decision makers, clients, past clients.
- To aid them in moving from one audience type to another
- To provide all the necessary elements required to assist them in 'their goals'

Ultimately your site, or web application, is there to serve your ideal audience. Not everyone in the world, not the largest possible audience in the world, but your audience. The audience that will better help you achieve your goals.

> *If you try to serve everyone,*
> *you'll serve no one.*

Who is it you are seeking to serve?

Not all sites sell products directly, there are many that serve only past customers by providing support and warranty services. There are blogs and news sites that sell 'content' and readership and monetize by advertising

Each site has its own audience type and segments of audience. A news site has people that have never heard of the site before, new readers, regular readers, past readers etc.

In this chapter will be working on outlining who it is you serve. We will be doing this by:

- Reviewing your existing customer base
- Learning more about who they are
- Digging into the problems they wanted solving when they came to you
- Defining what problems your existing solutions solve
- Reviewing gaps in what you currently offer and what your audience needs
- Identifying the ideal audience for your site
- Building personas based around the people we've defined and their needs

At the end of the chapter you will have a much better understanding of your specific audience/s that will guide you through the later sections of this workbook.

With a better understanding of the different groups you seek to serve you will be able to better prepare a sitemap that can cater for them. This will influence all your later decisions including functionality, design and most importantly the content you will create for them.

When you get into the site architecture and scoping processes later in this book you will be making decisions at a much more granular level, each page will be focused on its own goal for its own audience.

➤ Understanding Your Existing Audience

Throughout this book we work on exercises that are described and exampled as if you had an existing business, and existing site and products. This might not be the case, especially for those of you with a startup, a new business idea or a new product to develop and launch.

I would recommend you go back and read No Existing Website, Page 4 in the Introduction before proceeding further. In that chapter I have quickly reviewed each of the steps from the perspective of that point of view. Then you can continue on through the exercises with your frame of reference.

Existing verse Ideal Customers

You will start defining your audience by first documenting information about your existing customers.

Importantly this step is about gathering information about exactly who your existing customers are, and not an ideal customer. We will address ideal customers later in this section of the book.

Who is it you currently serve in your business? Who are the customers that you have now or have had previously? These are people who have actually either transacted with your business or in the case of a site that produces content, have subscribed and regularly engage with your content.

Define your existing customers?

This exercise begins by naming your existing customers. This is much easier if you are a business that sells products or services as you will have transaction records in your accounting or customer relationship management software.

If you are a site that doesn't sell products, for example a news/blog site then you will need to create names for the segments of people you are already aware of. If you have conducted surveys, polls or other readership based data gathering exercises you have names you can use or groups of readers you can name. e.g. Single Mums, Married Women etc.

Write down the names of your customers, the individuals or the business names if you sell products.

Record everything you can from many different snapshots of customers. Don't just focus on those that are the top sales, but also the worst. It is as important to gain understanding the audiences you currently serve but don't wish to, as it is the ones you do want to serve. Additionally taking note of underperforming sections of your business helps you to create ways to improve these in the new site.

Where can you gather this information?

- Customer sales reports
- Product sales volume reports
- Online sales reports
- Customer surveys
- Analytics reports
- Calling customers or doing site visits.

In **The Complete Website Planning Guide** this data is found in the chapter on Research. It is some of the most important groundwork you can do.

Think of products as what you are 'selling' on your site. It could be the articles people read, sign-ups to your newsletter, comments, reviews etc.

If you have both online and offline transactions then make sure the data is reflective of all sides of the business. We want to know your entire customer base.

Biggest Customers by $ Value

_____

_____

_____

_____

_____

_____

_____

_____

Most Products Sold

_____

_____

_____

_____

_____

_____

_____

_____

Biggest Customers by Volume

_____
_____
_____
_____
_____
_____
_____
_____

Most Profitable Customers

_____
_____
_____
_____
_____
_____
_____
_____

(more)

Least Profitable Customers

_____

_____

_____

_____

_____

_____

_____

_____

Worst Product Sales

_____

_____

_____

_____

_____

_____

_____

_____

Fill in any lists that make sense for your business, including most profitable products, least profitable products or customers. Five (5) on any list should be enough to help you see any trends or important data that will be useful in the next pages.

Additional Lists

List Name:

_____

_____

_____

_____

_____

_____

_____

_____

List Name:

_____

_____

_____

_____

_____

_____

_____

_____

List Name:

_____
_____
_____
_____
_____
_____
_____
_____
_____

List Name:

_____
_____
_____
_____
_____
_____
_____
_____
_____

List Name:

_____
_____
_____
_____
_____
_____
_____
_____

List Name:

_____
_____
_____
_____
_____
_____
_____
_____

➤ Who Are They?

Behind every transaction, page view and statistic used for measuring website performance there is a person.

The most important fact to remember while planning your site is that you are building it for humans, for people that need a problem solved.

In the previous exercise you created lists of either people or businesses that have a history with your organization.

For each of the businesses you listed you need to understand that behind that business is the person who makes the decision to use you to meet their needs. These people are the ones you need to create profiles on and look for the similarities and differences that will guide you in gaining deeper understanding of your existing audience.

By building a profile of these people and how they interact with your business you will gain useful insights that will become critical as you complete this website plan.

Profiling people

We'll start this process initially by giving them a name, a role and some simple demographic information.

These tables should be filled in with what you know now; you will be enhancing this data in subsequent steps.

Each step in the subsequent sections will build more information onto this base. Fill in each of the fields as you go, but where you might miss one element don't allow it to hold you up.

Keep working through the lists, adding more on each pass.

In the next pages you will start identifying base information about individuals that buy from you. It is not intended to be comprehensive; it's a starting point. By keeping it simple you should be able to get started without delay.

Talk to your client support and sales teams to get their answers to the fields where possible.

Example Table

First Name	M / F	Age	Role	Source	Other relelvant criteria
Mary	F	45+	CFO	referral	makes all the final purchase decisions
John	M	38	Warehouse manager	online	it's all about speed of delivery to him

Use these pages to start enhancing the information you completed in the previous section.

First Name	M / F	Age	Role	Source	Other relelvant criteria

First Name	M / F	Age	Role	Source	Other relelvant criteria

First Name	M / F	Age	Role	Source	Other relelvant criteria

What's Their Problem?

Not only do we need to know the necessary personal information about the people buying from our business, but we also need to understand why they came to us. In doing so, we are looking to understand the underlying problem they had that needed solving.

Why are they your clients? What is it about your product (or service) that solved their problem? Was it a good fit, or was it the closest solution they could find?

As you delve into the whys relating to their purchase you will be learning a lot about more than just what was sold.

Let's start with the problem they had that drove them into looking for a solution.

You will need to begin by contacting as many existing clients you can and ask them to provide useful answers to questions about the purchase they made.

You may find that your sales team already have some information about the whys. It is most likely you will need to make contact with people and ask them questions to get the answers you need.

Throughout this chapter, there are several pieces of information you want to gather, so before making contact do a read-through so that you have a list of questions to ask. You might only get one opportunity to get this information, so make it count.

While assumptions you might have can be a starting point when working through your client data, it isn't always correct. You need to ask real people for the real reasons they came to you. Within their answers will be other gems that you haven't thought you need to know yet.

Tip: Imagine if in your new site you had a method (or process) that allowed you to collect this sort of information when you made a sale. It would give you instant market research to add insight on how your market is working and changes that might be occurring in it.

List out the people you have received answers from and the problem they had.

Who	Problem they had
Billy	wants to be able to test his own water
Jane	dirty pool

First Name	Problem They have

(more)

First Name	Problem They have

➤ Customer Snapshots

These aren't Personas

Later in this workbook you will be filling out personas for your audience. A persona outlines many attributes and behaviors of our ideal clients or target audience. Personas help you to think of your clients as whole people and not just a data point from a sales chart.

Personas help us to understand who we are targeting, how they might be thinking, how we should communicate with them, and get us to shift into an empathetic mindset to help us be better in our marketing work.

The snapshots you are about to create are a stepping-stone on the path to creating the personas. You will start with the basic profiles and add to them as you move through the workbook. At this stage we want you to begin to see a broader view of why they have chosen your business.

What motivations have pushed them to come to your business?

> ### *What we think <-> What the facts tell us*

The closer to the truth you get in your research you will discover that often your gut feelings or prior knowledge that guided you in your decision-making might be flawed. The actual facts you discover will be current information about why existing customers are making the decisions they are.

There will be reasoning behind some of their decisions that hasn't been recognized previously or forgotten when generalizations have been made. All of us have our own biased assumptions and opinions on why people behave the way they do.

In order to create something better than before we want to uncover what is real and what might be an old piece of data that has just outlived its usefulness.

People are much more three-dimensional in both their needs and how they interact with your business than any simple outline we can come up with in our own heads. By asking them for their reasons and motivations we can open up many opportunities we haven't seen before.

Name (if known)_____ Mary Jones_____

Company_____ Big Company_____

Age   45+   Gender   F

What their problem was_____ Overweight and feel like rubbish_____

What they buy_____ Personal Training Sessions_____

How often _____ Monthly_____

What value do they buy?_____ $80 per session_____

Customer Snapshot Example

How to use the Customer Snapshots.

Using the information you have already gathered in previous exercises, fill in the following information to build out a snapshot for each person you have identified.

Where you don't have the answer to one of the fields, leave it blank but come back to it once you have gathered the information.

Key questions explained:

What their problem was: What was the problem they had before they came to you? What was the initial trigger that got them looking for a solution?

What they buy: Is it a product or a service, a subscription or something else?

How often: How often do they buy from you? Daily, weekly, monthly or once every few years etc?

The value they buy: What's the monetary value they spend with you, or if you were a news site or blog, how many articles per day/week on average do they read etc? Just use round numbers for this.

Name (if known)_____

Company_____

Age [   ]   Gender [   ]

What their problem was_____

What they buy_____

How often_____

What value do they buy?_____

Customer Snapshot 1

Name (if known)_____

Company_____

Age [   ]   Gender [   ]

What their problem was_____

What they buy_____

How often_____

What value do they buy?_____

Customer Snapshot 2

Name (if known)_____

Company_____

Age [   ]   Gender [   ]

What their problem was_____

What they buy_____

How often_____

What value do they buy?_____

Customer Snapshot 3

Name (if known)_____

Company_____

Age [   ]   Gender [   ]

What their problem was_____

What they buy_____

How often_____

What value do they buy?_____

Customer Snapshot 4

Name (if known)_____

Company_____

Age [ ]   Gender [ ]

What their problem was_____

What they buy_____

How often_____

What value do they buy?_____

Customer Snapshot 5

Name (if known)_____

Company_____

Age [ ]   Gender [ ]

What their problem was_____

What they buy_____

How often_____

What value do they buy?_____

Customer Snapshot 6

Name (if known)_____

Company_____

Age [   ]   Gender [   ]

What their problem was_____

What they buy_____

How often_____

What value do they buy?_____

Customer Snapshot 7

Name (if known)_____

Company_____

Age [   ]   Gender [   ]

What their problem was_____

What they buy_____

How often_____

What value do they buy?_____

Customer Snapshot 8

➤ Digging Deeper

The customer snapshots you have just completed are an early form of persona. They don't offer full insight to the individuals you have listed, but they are the beginning of something deeper.

In the following sections of this book, you will be broadening these snapshots. In doing so, your understanding of your clients will increase, and how you are currently treating them.

Why do we want to create these personas?

Successful marketing is built around an understanding of the people you are aiming to serve — your audience.

It is easy to see them only as someone who buys from you, not as three-dimensional people with many choices and needs.

When you learn to see them in the context of their world, their problems and needs, your place as their provider has more background. Not only will you have more knowledge about your role with them, but also with other people similar to them.

In the previous exercise, we added what the problem was they had that you were able to solve.

What we don't fully know though is how well this solution solved their problem and the broader context to that problem. A simple approach would be to stop with what we know now, and our target audience is everyone that has the same problem.

That is how other people look at their marketing. That is how many other websites are built. I have product X, it's there so the people who need an X to fix Y can buy it.

Digger deeper, as this section is named, is about you looking at the actual reason they might be, or have been, buying what you have to offer.

As we know, your customer typically starts with a problem they want to solve. In some cases that problem is as simple as, are there tickets still available to the movie? In many cases, there is an underlying problem they need to solve; that's why they started looking around.

They are seeking a solution to a more significant issue. In the example of the movie, the problem could be that they are bored; it could be they want to entertain a partner or any number of combinations of things.

Your job is to understand this broader problem more than just 'they wanted to buy movie tickets'.

Marketing to people who are fans of a particular actor is different to people that want to go to a movie every week for something to do. Their needs concerning the experience they are purchasing are quite different.

Think about the way you could create marketing offers and content to someone that wants an affordable weekly option, over people that are a super-fan of a particular actor.

The example above is simplistic, but the principles are the same no matter what product or service you have.

One of the goals of you creating your website plan is so that your website will get you better results. Which will mean you build a site with a purpose, and your online shop won't just have a bunch of products loaded up hoping someone will buy them.

You will be building a site offering solutions to people's problems based on you understanding more detail about those problems and surrounding needs.

It also helps you to make sure you are trying to service the right people for the way you run your business.

The word "problem" sounds as if it is something negative. It isn't; it is merely an issue that needs a resolution. Being hungry isn't negative; it happens multiple times a day for billions of people. The question of "What shall I eat right now?" isn't a negative; it is just a problem that in theory will be solved.

In **The Complete Website Planning Guide**, most of this work you are doing now was in the single chapter titled Research. In this workbook, you will find research in many of the chapters. The keys to successful marketing and by extension, website development is knowing your audience better, which means more research!

In a series of steps, you will:

- review your existing products/services to see what you think they solve
- expand on the customer snapshots to go into more depth on the problems
- get more understanding of how your customers are drawn to you or your competitors
- identify gaps between what your audience wants and what you provide
- complete the personas for your business

Through the process, you will outline a range of problems and variations of issues relating to them, which will provide the framework for subsequent chapters.

While completing this work, you will likely get insights into variations of that problem of the customer you are interviewing. Write them down as well. These are essential insights that show you are putting yourself into the shoes of others.

Later in this workbook, when we address site functionality and the content that goes with it, these insights will create additional possibilities for you.

For example, guides, checklists and FAQ content often are easily derived from the problems you hear from real customers. It also helps you see all the shortfalls your current site might have and why it isn't appealing to a broader group of people.

The research you are about to do will provide the framework for the subsequent chapters.

What Problems Are You Currently Solving?

This section is about clarifying what you already offer and what problems you believe it is solving.

The plan you are building isn't made in isolation of your existing business. It is about improving how your company operates online by creating an improved website.

We've identified the initial problems that customers have determined helped to bring them to your business.

Now you will identify each of your products or services and list what types of problems you think they solve. Use both the issues you've heard from your customers as well as any other you consider relevant.

Creating a matrix of what you sell and what people need is an essential step in clarifying what you are working on as well as identifying gaps.

Consider all of your products/services, not just those which you already sell on your existing site. You might think one of your services will never sell online, but don't prejudge anything, go through the exercises with an open mind.

There might be a range of products or services you wish you were selling more of or content that you want more people to read.

While a lot of the plan you will work on is externally focused, you mustn't lose sight of the things you need to sell that will make you more successful.

➤ What Do You Want To Provide?

Write down every product or service that you would like to generate more sales for from your website.

What Problem Do These Products Solve?

Now that you have a list of the products or services that you want to sell more of, you now want to identify what types of problems they solve.

You will relate these to the problems your customers previously told you about as well as others you believe you solve.

It is a valuable exercise in learning to identify gaps in how you see your market and how your market sees you.

Using the knowledge from your customers, or from speaking to team members in your organization, write down first the product and then the problem/s you believe it solves.

This role of this step is that you challenge yourself to think of as many possible problems you consider your products solve.

These are features or benefits; they are the problems it solves. Selling a gym membership has many benefits and potential benefits. E.g. losing weight or getting stronger. The problem the user might have is that they have a sore back, or that they don't like themselves due to their weight, or they can't play with their kids as readily as they once could.

You might find it beneficial to first write down the features and benefits of your products on a separate page before considering how these might solve problems for people.

You will find if you allow yourself time to come up with ideas you will start to get inspiration about possible problems that had never occurred to you before.

Not so many years ago, people that worked shift work had a problem that gyms were never open for them when they needed them to be. Now we have 24-hour gyms. Someone identified this problem, how many people it affected and worked on a solution.

There are multiple lines per product so you can record as many issues as you need.

Product	
Problem Solved by Product	

Product	
Problem Solved by Product	

Product	
Problem Solved by Product	

Product	
Problem Solved by Product	

Product	
Problem Solved by Product	

Product	
Problem Solved by Product	

Product	
Problem Solved by Product	

Product	
Problem Solved by Product	

(more)

Product	
Problem Solved by Product	

Product	
Problem Solved by Product	

Product	
Problem Solved by Product	

Product	
Problem Solved by Product	

Product	
Problem Solved by Product	

Product	
Problem Solved by Product	

Product	
Problem Solved by Product	

Product	
Problem Solved by Product	

(more)

Product	
Problem Solved by Product	

Product	
Problem Solved by Product	

Product	
Problem Solved by Product	

Product	
Problem Solved by Product	

Product	
Problem Solved by Product	

Product	
Problem Solved by Product	

Product	
Problem Solved by Product	

Product	
Problem Solved by Product	

➤ Understanding Your Customer's Problems

You will put aside the work you've just completed around your products for the time being while expanding on the snapshots you drafted earlier.

Each of these recent exercises has been about listing the potential problems customers have. Next, we want to review those problems in more detail.

Knowing there is a problem is only the first step towards a more in-depth understanding. You need to go behind that problem to find the specific personal details that relate to this issue.

You need to be able to empathize with your customers, to see the problem in their eyes and not in your company view. The company view tends to be singularly focused; **our {widget} fixes this {thing/problem}.**

A human being is more complex than this, and individual circumstances heavily influence their decision-making processes.

In the example on the next page, the problem and solution seem simple. Jenny has a dirty pool, so the answer is to clean it.

Why isn't Jenny cleaning the pool? There could be many possible answers to that question:

- Does she have a physical disability that prevents her from being able to?
- Is she afraid of water?
- Does she not know how to keep it clean?
- Is her budget so tiny she can't afford the chemicals needed?
- Or...?

You can see that while the problem is about the pool being dirty, there can be a lot more to consider as to the underlying cause.

Not only is there a cause, but there are also additional consequences to the pool remaining dirty that will be affecting Jenny emotionally.

No one wants to see a filthy green pool in their backyard every day to remind them they aren't successful or have other issues. We all have to deal with the reality of life, but there's nothing worse than having it shoved in your face every day.

As soon as you recognize that there are emotional considerations to be aware of you can then understand that a one-size-fits-all model of selling might work against you.

There are now other obstacles and considerations you need to be aware of. When you learn more about these sides of the buyer, you can consider how to write the content and what types of offers you can present. You will begin to see new opportunities that you had not previously considered.

Buy now pay later options were created to allow people with limited budgets the opportunity to take action immediately. That is an obvious example, but there are numerous ways you can review the problem and see how your company can provide a suitable solution.

We'll look into solutions a little later on; for now, work through each of the problems you have identified and expand on them.

➤ Understanding Problems

Below is just an example of how one product might be solving many different problems.

Jenny, our fictional mom, has a dirty pool, and the story behind this is entirely different to other customers of our pool products. Right now, we only want to focus on Jenny's problem and write down everything we can find out from her about it.

Jenny's Problem

Their Name Jenny

What was their problem? Pool is always dirty

Why was this a problem? Doesn't get used, she hates looking at it, feels bad because she can't do anything about it but can't hide from it. Thinking about moving.

What was in the way of them having this problem solved? Kids are too young to do it, she doesn't have time to do it, little spare money to have someone else do it.

Why? Recently separated and struggling to handle everything on her own, doesn't want to move becuase the kids have been through enough but money is super tight

What were their options at the time? sell the house and move, do it herself, empty the pool

How did our product/service change this for them? they were able to stay where thery were and enjoy the pool. requires little maintenence and has easy to understand videos explaining what to do and on a payment plan.

Customer Problem 1

Their Name

What was their problem?

Why was this a problem?

What was in the way of them having this problem solved?.

Why?

What were their options at the time?

How did our product/service change this for them?

Customer Problem 2

Their Name

What was their problem?

Why was this a problem?

What was in the way of them having this problem solved?.

Why?

What were their options at the time?

How did our product/service change this for them?

(more)

Customer Problem 3

Their Name

What was their problem?

Why was this a problem?

What was in the way of them having this problem solved?.

Why?

What were their options at the time?

How did our product/service change this for them?

Customer Problem 4

Their Name

What was their problem?

Why was this a problem?

What was in the way of them having this problem solved?.

Why?

What were their options at the time?

How did our product/service change this for them?

(more)

Customer Problem 5

Their Name

What was their problem?

Why was this a problem?

What was in the way of them having this problem solved?.

Why?

What were their options at the time?

How did our product/service change this for them?

Customer Problem 6

Their Name

What was their problem?

Why was this a problem?

What was in the way of them having this problem solved?.

Why?

What were their options at the time?

How did our product/service change this for them?

(more) ➤

Customer Problem 7

Their Name

What was their problem?

Why was this a problem?

What was in the way of them having this problem solved?.

Why?

What were their options at the time?

How did our product/service change this for them?

Customer Problem 8

Their Name

What was their problem?

Why was this a problem?

What was in the way of them having this problem solved?.

Why?

What were their options at the time?

How did our product/service change this for them?

(more) ➤

Customer Problem 9

Their Name

What was their problem?

Why was this a problem?

What was in the way of them having this problem solved?.

Why?

What were their options at the time?

How did our product/service change this for them?

Spotting the Gaps

Now that you have expanded on your view of your customer's problems, we will want to compare this to the review you conducted of your products.

This review will allow you to identify any gaps you might have in your product, or service, offering.

It will also identify if we need to speak to more customers to get a broader perspective on their problems.

In this section, you will list each problem that your customers mentioned to you and match it to a product or service that you are offering.

This exercise will help you identify customer problems you have no solution for as well as recognizing how many issues your products are helping to solve. You are helping people, but often you don't know why, so seeing it laid out before you will help you in the future planning exercises.

As you conduct more research, you will invariably be looking at competitors' sites, and speaking to new prospects and customers with questions in your mind. You will see or learn other problems that people have which you had not considered before. Make sure to add all of these to your list.

You are ultimately creating a master list of individual problems that relate to the audience you are serving or wish to help.

In later exercises, you will group these problems to help you in our conceptual design process and content production.

Note. Problems you don't want to solve.

We've highlighted that it is likely you will find new opportunities when you learn about problems you don't have a solution for, yet. There is another side to this as well. You might identify problems you don't want to be solving, or cannot solve.

That's a positive byproduct of this research. You will be able to see there are sections of your marketplace where you are not the right solution provider. You can address this by making sure you don't attract that audience, or if you do, send them to someone that can help them.

We don't want to go to all this effort only to attract people to us whose needs can't be met by us.

Problem They Have	Matching Product / Service

Problem They Have	Matching Product / Service

(more)

Problem They Have	Matching Product / Service

Problem They Have	Matching Product / Service

(more)

Problem They Have	Matching Product / Service

Problem They Have	Matching Product / Service

(more)

➤ Personas

Personas give us an identity to frame our thinking around, like an actor in a play.

As you have gathered the more in-depth data about your existing clients, you should be starting to get a feel for who they are. In a broader sense, you see the demographic segments that make up your audience.

At first, you see products and products that fix something. Then you start to see broader groupings of people who have similar problems.

Homeowners with dirty pools are one example from our previous example.

It's easy to slip into the mindset of these segments being enough. And you will be better off using that level of market knowledge than just listing products on your site. It isn't the end goal we want, though.

Segmentation is an excellent way to make sure you understand a product and service-based approaches to your marketing, and that leads to the next part of this process which is developing individual personas.

When you produce content, of any type, for your site or offline marketing, taking the next step to fixate on an individual is much more powerful.

Why do we give them names and identities?

Creating names and identities for individual customers enables you to step into their shoes. It allows you to see the world through their perspective and take an outside-in approach to how you develop your site.

It is much easier to use a name when referring to what you are working on, than 'Profile C'.

➤ Sample Persona

This example is designed to help explain what information you are looking to learn from your clients. Note that the problem isn't that they didn't have your product, it's the problem that had them looking for a solution. In the example is that Jenny has a dirty pool. This leads on to her purchasing a solution from the company but in digging deeper into understanding the problem we learn a number of interesting pieces of information.

Name: _____

Age: _____

Job: _____

Income: _____ Gender: _____

Family: _____ Y/N   Kids: _____

Lives Where: _____

Summary: Give a summary of how they are today. Might be health, money, relationships, something relevant to what area of their life your product matches to. For B2B this would highlight more about their approach to work, business and what their current situation in their business is.

Life Choices: Describe their life choices, things they do, products/brands they like, things they want to do/ choose to do, etc. We want to understand more about how and why they do the things they do.

Work Story: Where do they work, if they work, how long, how do they feel about it, what is good/ bad about their working life? Be specific about the business, name it if necessary or the type of business e.g. Plumbing firm with 20 staff based in Brisbane.

Current Problem/Issues That Relate To Your Product(s).
What problems in their life/ business do your products address? What problem/s do they have and how do they feel about those problems? Why are they ideal for your product? Focus on ONE primary problem.

What Could Happen If This Issue Isn't Resolved?
Talk about how they would feel, their family would feel, how people would react, what other costs might there be for them. financial, professional, personal. What are they afraid of?

What Could/Would Happen If The Problem Were Solved
What happens when it is solved? Or what would the ideal solution look/ feel like? How would the client feel, what will happen to them at work, personally, etc?

In A Nutshell:
Summarize your Jenny in a succinct way that you can refer back to. This should be a concise and potent sum up of Jenny and her major problem that you can validate your decisions from. It should be as if she said it, not you!

Persona 1

Name:_____

Age: _____

Job: _____

Income:_____ Gender:_____

Family: _____ Y / N Kids:_____

Lives Where:_____

Summary:_____
_____

Life Choices:_____
_____

Work Story:_____
_____

Current Problem / Issues That Relate To Your Product(s):_____
_____

What Could Happen If This Issue Isn't Resolved?_____
_____

What Could / Would Happen If The Problem Were Solved?_____
_____

In A Nutshell:_____
_____
_____

Persona 2

Name:_____

Age: _____

Job: _____

Income:_____ Gender:_____

Family: _____ Y / N   Kids:_____

Lives Where:_____

Summary:_____

Life Choices:_____

Work Story:_____

Current Problem / Issues That Relate To Your Product(s):_____

What Could Happen If This Issue Isn't Resolved?_____

What Could / Would Happen If The Problem Were Solved?_____

In A Nutshell:_____

(more) ▶

Persona 3

Name:

Age:

Job:

Income: Gender:

Family: Y / N   Kids:

Lives Where:

Summary:

Life Choices:

Work Story:

Current Problem / Issues That Relate To Your Product(s):

What Could Happen If This Issue Isn't Resolved?

What Could / Would Happen If The Problem Were Solved?

In A Nutshell:

Persona 4

Name:_____

Age: _____

Job: _____

Income:_____ Gender:_____

Family:_____ Y / N   Kids:_____

Lives Where:_____

Summary:_____
_____

Life Choices:_____
_____

Work Story:_____
_____

Current Problem / Issues That Relate To Your Product(s):_____
_____

What Could Happen If This Issue Isn't Resolved?_____
_____

What Could / Would Happen If The Problem Were Solved?_____
_____

In A Nutshell:_____
_____
_____

(more) ➤

Persona 5

Name:_____

Age:_____

Job:_____

Income:_____ Gender:_____

Family:_____ Y / N   Kids:_____

Lives Where:_____

Summary:_____

Life Choices:_____

Work Story:_____

Current Problem / Issues That Relate To Your Product(s):_____

What Could Happen If This Issue Isn't Resolved?_____

What Could / Would Happen If The Problem Were Solved?_____

In A Nutshell:_____

Persona 6

Name:_____

Age: _____

Job: _____

Income:_____ Gender:_____

Family:_____ Y / N   Kids:_____

Lives Where:_____

Summary:

Life Choices:

Work Story:

Current Problem / Issues That Relate To Your Product(s):

What Could Happen If This Issue Isn't Resolved?

What Could / Would Happen If The Problem Were Solved?

In A Nutshell:

(more) ➤

Persona 7

Name:_____

Age: _____

Job: _____

Income:_____ Gender:_____

Family: _____ Y / N   Kids:_____

Lives Where: _____

Summary:

Life Choices:

Work Story:

Current Problem / Issues That Relate To Your Product(s):

What Could Happen If This Issue Isn't Resolved?

What Could / Would Happen If The Problem Were Solved?

In A Nutshell:

Persona 8

Name:_____

Age: _____

Job: _____

Income:_____ Gender:_____

Family: _____ Y / N   Kids:_____

Lives Where:_____

Summary:_____
_____

Life Choices:_____
_____

Work Story:_____
_____

Current Problem / Issues That Relate To Your Product(s):_____
_____

What Could Happen If This Issue Isn't Resolved?_____
_____

What Could / Would Happen If The Problem Were Solved?_____
_____

In A Nutshell:_____
_____
_____

(more) ▶

Persona 9

Name:_____

Age: _____

Job: _____

Income:_____ Gender:_____

Family:_____ Y / N   Kids:_____

Lives Where:_____

Summary:_____

Life Choices:_____

Work Story:_____

Current Problem / Issues That Relate To Your Product(s):_____

What Could Happen If This Issue Isn't Resolved?_____

What Could / Would Happen If The Problem Were Solved?_____

In A Nutshell:_____

Persona 10

Name:_____

Age: _____

Job: _____

Income:_____ Gender:_____

Family: _____ Y / N   Kids:_____

Lives Where:_____

Summary:_____

Life Choices:_____

Work Story:_____

Current Problem / Issues That Relate To Your Product(s):_____

What Could Happen If This Issue Isn't Resolved?_____

What Could / Would Happen If The Problem Were Solved?_____

In A Nutshell:_____

MUST HAVES

What Must Your Business Have?

Must-haves are those items which your website must have. Seems obvious and it is a simple concept.

Individual businesses have their own specific needs and requirements. Sometimes these are operational; other times, they might be part of a broader strategy.

For example, a kitchen appliance business might note in all their product literature that you can get a replacement copy of your manual on their website.

In this instance, product manuals in pdf format is a **must-have** item.

It is essential to list out these must-haves, so they become part of the scope. If they aren't part of the scope, then there is a high likelihood of them being overlooked.

You need to go through all of the things that your business needs on the site. These are items which cannot be removed or compromised.

In your completed scope document, there will be some wishlist items. Once you have the project quoted there might be items that will get excluded; must-have items are those that you won't remove.

They can be as simple as separate inquiry forms for different sections of the site, or a newsletter sign-up panel. They might be as complicated as a customer portal to view all invoices and statements.

Review all of the internal requests and feedback you have gathered. Look at the content that has performed on your existing site, and think about elements of your organization's workflow to create the list of items.

Example Must-Haves

- Newsletter sign-up form
  Add a newsletter sign-up form in the footer of each page

- Accept Terms & Conditions to submit an order
  When a user is on the checkout page they must check a checkbox to accept the Terms & Conditions to be able to submit their order.

- Free Resources Section
  Section of the website that has free resources to be downloaded.

- Collect email address to download free item
  A site visitor must provide their email address before being able to access the resource

List out each item that is a must-have for your website in the Item field (e.g. Item 1) and then describe it in the description panel.

Make sure you outline the key information that will help everyone understand the importance of each item

If you need more space you can download the template from **https://ireck.in/wpgwork**

Must-Have Item 1	
Description of Item	

Must-Have Item 2	
Description of Item	

Must-Have Item 3	
Description of Item	

Must-Have Item 4	
Description of Item	

Must-Have Item 5	
Description of Item	

Must-Have Item 6	
Description of Item	

Must-Have Item 7	
Description of Item	

Must-Have Item 8	
Description of Item	

Must-Have Item 9	
Description of Item	

Must-Have Item 10	
Description of Item	

Must-Have Item 11	
Description of Item	

Must-Have Item 12	
Description of Item	

Must-Have Item 13	
Description of Item	

Must-Have Item 14	
Description of Item	

Must-Have Item 15	
Description of Item	

RESEARCH

Researching Your Market

You have already been researching this workbook, and this chapter continues that with more focus on your existing site.

You will be working on gathering useful information about how users are using your existing sites. If you are working on a new concept, the same methods can be used to user test your prototypes.

As you work through this chapter, apply the method, or way of thinking, to the tools available to you. For example, if you don't have Google Analytics installed on your site, but have alternative analytics and user test tools, then use that data.

> *Data well interpreted will guide you*
> *better than guesswork*

Throughout this book, we mention commonly used tools as examples. The tool itself isn't the important item; it is the principle of what you are using it for that matters most.

It's a workbook, so cross out the name and label it according to the tools you have available to you.

The data you will be looking at here is actual usage data. You should be trying to see correctly how real people are using your site. Similarly to how you test new design concepts, if you don't have existing site data, you can get user testing feedback on prototypes.

The key to research is doing it with real people and gathering real data. It is not about your gut feelings or the thoughts of your boss; this is about gathering factual information to help you make informed professional decisions.

Before web user testing and analytics tools came into existence, businesses relied on focus groups and the like.

The type of research you will doing for this scope is one-to-one interviews or sessions. You will be accessing existing measurement tools and analyzing essential information.

You need to be able to see real statistics and usage of your site. A common mistake is to use your own experience or to make guesses based on the endpoint data.

Take the time and extra effort to dig into all of the available information, and you will add critical insights to your planning process.

➤ Gathering Information

In this chapter, you will be gathering lots of information from a range of sources. The pages that follow will allow you to record the essential statistics or observations so you can use them in later stages of the plan.

You don't need to worry about your level of expertise when doing this research. While knowing the tools is helpful, most of the knowledge you will use comes from learning what the data tells you about your site.

At this point, your knowledge of your audience might be small, so each new observation made increases your understanding. Each incremental learning can only improve the results.

Analytics software might appear challenging at first, but there is a myriad of helpful posts on the internet to help you. This workbook couldn't cover enough to teach you all about the software and the many ways you can use it. Learn enough to get the data out and focus on the most relevant data.

Once you begin, you will find that the tools are logical and provide a wealth of insight. As your confidence grows you will learn more and more about your site and how it performs.

The following pages will encourage you to use the following tools:

Analytics for:

- Content performance
- Goals
- Pathways
- Audience
- Device statistics
- Demographics

Usability Tools for:

- Navigation
- Lost opportunities
- Sticking points or problems in design
- General User behavior
- Form analysis
- Funnel analysis

We will also consider polls and surveys to uncover sales objections and obstacles from users.

You will need to gather as much useful information as possible without getting bogged down in numbers. Knowing that the home page on your site gets the most hits isn't necessarily very useful on its own. Knowing that 60% of people go from the home page to another page is more important.

Reading every answer in a poll or survey might not be the best use of your time, but you can use software to analyze it and find the trends. You can then also review the outliers and look through the custom comments in the surveys to find other gems.

In later chapters in the book when you need to reference key observations easily, you will better understand why we are recording them in many lists.

Content Performance

Part of our planning for a new site needs to include understanding which content on your existing website is working and what isn't.

Using analytics software, we can review how different content on the site gets used. Each page on your website is tracked and can tell you many stories about how users access it and what value it has to them.

There are commonly discussed numbers like page views and hits, but there is a lot more to be discovered by going below the surface within your analytics tool.

A well-trafficked page will also tell us about its bounce rate, and other pages users come from or go to in their journey through your site. These pathways are as important as the numbers of people visiting. They provide insight into how the content is working, or not.

We want to evaluate content in the following ways at least:

- Most trafficked pages
- Best performing Landing Pages
- Worst performing Landing pages
- Bounce rate (lowest and highest) of pages
- Which pages seem to contribute most to successful user pathways.

Notes:

What is a landing page?

Is the first page viewed in a user session. The entry point to your website.

What is bounce rate?

It is the **percentage** of visits in which a person leaves your website from the landing page without browsing any further

What is a user pathway?

The Users Flow report is a graphical representation of the paths users took through your site, from the source, through the various pages, and where along their paths they exited your site

➤ Most Visited Pages

Firstly list the most visited pages on the site (note the url `/` in Analytics denotes the home page of your site).

List as many as makes sense for the size of the site you are evaluating. A smaller site might only require you to list the top 10 pages, whereas a larger site might be the top 50.

Page Name	URL	Visits

➤ Top Landing Pages

Select the report for the most trafficked Landing Pages. You can filter these by source (where visitors came from) or other metrics the key objective here is to find the pages that are currently attracting the most content.

When we evaluate the best performing pages it makes sense to evaluate those that have the highest traffic first, the higher the number the more likely we will get a better picture of their performance.

Page Name	URL	Visits

(more) ➤

Page Name	URL	Visits

Lowest Bounce Rate

Bounce rates will vary for many different websites and types of sites. Different types of content, as well as the traffic sources and devices, will each have their specific bounce rate levels.

It pays not just to take the default filters at face value, and to change the filtering you use so you can review the bounce rates for your site.

For example, a blog site that relies on Facebook for a lot of its traffic will find that content has a very high bounce rate. That is because people are viewing the shared post in the Facebook app on their mobile device. They click to read it, read it, then return to Facebook.

So their behavior is very different from those who came to your site from search queries in search engines. Compare bounce rates for people who spent at least 5 seconds on your website to exclude possible bots that are not reading the content. You can also check by country or other types of segmentation to get different views on your content. Then record the pages that matter which have the lowest bounce rates.

Page Name	URL	Visits

(more) ➤

Page Name	URL	Visits

➤ Highest Bounce Rate

Record the pages with the highest bounce rate in this table, ignoring any that aren't useful. Often Analytics will have pages with query strings on the URLs or other pages that have a 100% bounce rate, but these aren't relevant for making content decisions.

Page Name	URL	Visits

(more) ➤

Page Name	URL	Visits

➤ Top Pages From Search

Understanding content that creates traffic from search engines is crucial to your planning. Firstly you don't want to lose that benefit if it's useful traffic about what you offer. By recording those that already perform, you can ensure that you maintain, if not improve, that performance.

Understanding what pages are already bringing you good traffic numbers will enable you to compare those pages with ones that aren't. This information will give you insights on how you might be able to replicate results from pages that have worked.

Look into Analytics and find the Sources reports, and look at which pages are coming from Organic search results. You will use these reports later to review other sources as well, e.g. Social.

Page Name	URL	Visits

(more) ➤

Page Name	URL	Visits

Most Important Pathway Pages

Pathways are the sequences of pages that users go through when on your site.

While users are all unique, and their needs individual, no matter the size of your site, you will find consistent pathways commonly used.

Observe people in parks, and you can see well-trodden pathways that groups make, from a common objective, the shortest path to the location they are heading to.

Looking at pathways through your site will reveal common pages that show up in many different visitor sessions.

Comparing pages that are visited more often to those that aren't will highlight parts of the site that need more focus in your future designs and copywriting. In particular, when you create your sitemaps, you will want to think about the pathways and how to improve them.

There will always be obvious pathways, e.g. 'add to the shopping cart and the cart page' for an e-commerce store, which you won't spend much time thinking about. It's the less obvious and essential pages across your site that you want to discover.

Page Name	URL	Visits

(more)

Page Name	URL	Visits

Demographic Information

If you have it enabled in Analytics for your site, then you can review Demographic information about the people visiting your website. You can also compile demographic information from customer data, by gender, age and other interest profile data you might have collected.

While this information might be well known within your business, adding it into your website plan helps to share this information with everyone involved in the development of your site. Such information will impact content, design and other factors, so make sure to include as much information as you can.

Page Name	URL	Visits

➤ Device Information

Record as much information as you can about the devices that get used on your site. Review not just the devices but look at screen sizes, bounce rates and other vital metrics segmented by device.

Knowing the performance based on the groups of audience will impact many design decisions later in your project.

Page Name	URL	Visits

Additional Data

The tables on the previous pages are just some of the ways you can classify the content on your site.

There are many other data points and ways to classify content within Analytics and other tracking programs you have.

For you to do that we've created a series of tables to fill in where you can create the labels and table headings as you see fit

Each business has its own data and areas that matter most to them. e.g. if social media has an influence on user behavior on your site, then you want to make sure you are tracking that as a source as well as how it influences the pathways and attribution in sales etc.

These sheets are also where you can record relevant keyword research or other search engine optimization data that you have gathered.

Hopefully, you have already audited your existing site from an SEO perspective, and those improvements are in your earlier lists.

If you haven't started gathering SEO improvement information, then you should stop and do so now. You should use either a specialist agency or some of the fantastic tools available to audit your existing site as well as gather what you need for the new site.

Now write down all relevant data you gathered in the following pages.

Page name	Social Media Source	% Add to Carts
dresses	instagram	17%
mens shorts	pinterest	5%

➤ Your Specific Data

There are many other data points and ways to classify content within Analytics and other tracking programs you have. The following sections include pages you can label to record what matters most for your website.

Table Name:_____

(more)

(more) ➤

(more)

(more)

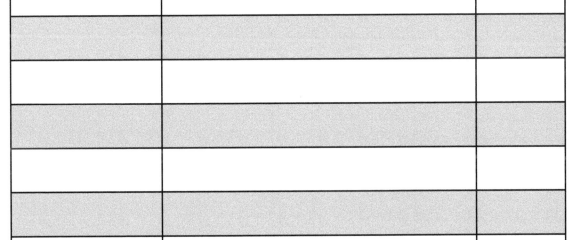

(more)

➤ User Behavior Observations

To see real users' behavior on your website, you will have to use either real-life monitoring or software solutions.

Trying to get enough real users where you can sit with them and observe them is difficult and often very impractical, especially with global users of a site.

The use of screen capture videos, heat maps and user testing services can provide a wealth of information for a fraction of the effort and cost.

These tools will not report numbers as analytics software does and in most cases, will require you to watch the videos. You will need to observe, and listen to if relevant, what is happening and record what activity is happening and trends.

It takes time to analyze but provides some of the richest insights you will get about how real people use your site.

I recommend you start with some sheets of spare paper and create notes about what you are watching. Then you can collate this data into your workbook once you have a good grasp on what you have been seeing.

It is very easy to make a decision based on one video, but that is not a good sample size. One video can show good or bad usage of your site, but it is not a big enough sample size. You need to watch and observe many of the videos to pick up on patterns of behavior.

Look for options that seem to be working well. Are there click patterns on a critical page that are showing how a limited selection of CTA's is guiding people deeper into sections of the site? Or is there a spread of clicks all over that page which highlights that users aren't sure what to do next.

Such observations can point to design issues, content problems or other usability issues. There's no right answer; there is just observation of a problem, then testing of a new hypothesis on how to resolve the problem.

Make observations and try to find the patterns. You can usually select videos that include the page you want to observe. Review different pages; look at everything from click patterns to content scroll.

Heatmaps will show you which parts of the page are getting the most visibility, click tracking will show exact places on a page that users click.

A common issue you can find is where users expect to be able to click on an image or heading, but only the 'Read More' link is clickable. It is a minor thing but when corrected, can reduce user friction on a website.

➤ Your Observations

Use the following pages to outline any relevant observations about user behavior, content, and other items you can determine from any form of user research.

It might be helpful to notate where the observation is from, i.e. what tool or process, so others can relate to the types of observations and the methods when reviewing the data

(more)

(more)

(more)

(more)

SORTING
THE DATA

➤ Time to Sort the Data

As you worked through the earlier chapters of this workbook, you have gathered and written down large amounts of data. You will have data about how your existing site performs, your existing clients and your target audience. You will have identified possible usability issues on your current website and must-have requirements for your new website.

At this point, it is all recorded on different pages and listed as you found it. Pages and pages of notes, edits and individual data points are difficult to use until you have sorted them.

The best websites are highly structured, well thought out hubs of information. They don't happen to be well architected by accident; they are planned this way and organized in ways that make sense for their purpose.

It's your turn now to start sorting through everything you have learned so far and to create the groups that will make the most sense for what you are trying to achieve.

There are many ways to sort data, and to collate different collections of information.

This workbook uses Affinity Diagrams to assemble the information into groupings that will inform decisions in the later stages of the scoping process.

We have two goals to achieve here:

1. To make sure we have a logical and coherent structure to our site

2. To allow us easy access to essential pieces of information without having to dig through a myriad of pages to find it.

Having been through this much effort already, you don't want to miss a critical item simply because it is hidden with other information.

This method of grouping information will help you spot trends and triggers for when you get to the functional scope and wireframe sections of the plan. It will give you the ability to scan over the vital information and find elements that will help achieve the page-by-page goals.

➤ Affinity Diagram

What is an affinity diagram?

An affinity diagram is a method used to sort large amounts of data into themes, or groups, based on their natural relationships. Once grouped, they can then be reviewed and analyzed.

An affinity board or sorting session can be done on paper, on a whiteboard, using a tool like Trello, or on a table. It is common for groups to use post-it notes stuck on a wall as their method while others use colored cards on a table.

How you do it is less important than doing it.

In this workbook, we have created columns which have multiple cells within them. Each column would be considered one group, or theme.

In the example below, I have prefilled some fictional content relating to a legal services business. This information relates to the legal area of will and estates, a service they offer. They have been researching how people, in general, think about wills and the services lawyers provide in this field.

The first column, Ungrouped, are items that they collected but are yet to be placed in any group. Typically this list would be extensive when you start, and it will empty as you sort the data.

It is possible that you might have a few items at the end of your first sorting process that still don't fit into any other group. That's OK, all the information you have gathered will be useful to you, whether it fits into a group or not.

I recommend you do more than one version of sorting your data if you have not done this type of exercise before. If you are doing it on your own, that will allow you to let the first sort percolate in your mind and to help you see fresh insights the next time through.

How to sort the data

1. Start by 'picking up' one piece of data and considering in what type of group it might belong. In the example, we selected 'Wills are for old people' and decided that this might belong in a group called 'Lack of Knowledge'.

2. Go to the next piece of data and review it. Does it belong in the column you have already created? If so, place it there. If not consider where it might belong. For 'Lawyers are Expensive' it could have been an issue because of a lack of knowledge, that kind of fits. Instead, we chose that the group 'Fear of Lawyers' was more suitable, and it belonged there.

3. Continue this process through each of the cards (pieces of information).

4. As you work through the diagram, you will come up with new groups for a data item which might be more suitable for data you have already sorted. That is normal during this process. Move it into the new group.

5. If you are unsure what to name groups, you can leave them blank until later in the process. Group data together because you think it is logical that they go together then come back and review the groups later. The description, or name, might be easier to apply then.

6. Some groups name themselves, such as Usability or Mobile. However, if they are content-focused groups, you might need more effort to sort the groups and create names.

Use as many columns as necessary to help sort your data. You can put small post-it notes onto the pages, but don't worry about making changes, there's a downloadable template you can also use.

You will want to make changes as you work through it, use as many as you need initially then go back through them to see if you can condense the groups further.

There is no prescribed number of columns you should use. This exercise is to place all of the data you have uncovered into easily accessible and logical groups. You want to be able to see the data, and particularly the themes, readily when you head into the later chapters.

Keep reviewing and working on it until you have created the right groups that offer you insight into your audience. However you sort the data, you need to be able to translate these groups into actionable and useful parts of your site.

Not only will you see a theme, but you may then uncover topics for which you have no data yet.

Using the legal example we have, the column 'Lack of Knowledge' tells us topics that we consider stem from people's lack of knowledge. What it doesn't answer though is why they have this lack of knowledge.

When you head into your content production stage, having this insight may drive more research to understand why they have such a lack of knowledge. They may have had bad experiences.

Some of these pieces of data might belong in this affinity diagram, and you can fill it in, others might need to be placed elsewhere for use later.

When you see data like this, it becomes much easier to understand areas you will need to address. While anyone could suggest that having a piece of content informing about the value of having a will makes sense, the insights about why it's essential should drive the differing types of material needed to move someone from not understanding the value of a will to the types of value it provides.

One piece of content is not likely to handle all the issues and perspectives of people.

You may have a separate affinity diagram just about lack of knowledge regarding wills grouped by the types of people.

Those groups might be: Under 30, 31-50, 50-65, Retirees.

Under these headings, you might have many different cards that outline the issues each age group has.

Thus sorting your data is not only one-dimensional. In the first pass, you are trying to group the higher-level aspects of your research, and then where there is a high volume of information, you should be breaking it down into smaller sections of information that will provide you with the most significant insights.

Don't worry while we have provided several pages to fill in for this process; there's also a link to a template you can download and print off to supplement your needs.

Example Affinity Diagram

The following diagram shows how a typical affinity diagram is laid out. You create columns with headings that are your 'groups' within which are individual data cards.

Ungrouped	Lack of Knowledge	Fear of Lawyers
We aren't married	Wills are for old people	Lawyers are expensive
I'm just a young guy	We don't have any assets	The lawyer will take control of my assets
Why can't I write up my own will?	Health directives are for sick people	
Wills should be free		
What is a power of attorney?		

➤ Sorting the Data

➤ Finalizing Your Research.

Creating affinity diagrams will have helped you to group a lot of the information you have gathered. You should now be able to see common themes relating to the research you have conducted.

As you worked through creating the diagrams and earlier stages of your research, you likely made other notes that don't fit into this format.

We have left a series of pages blank at the end of this section of the workbook for you to capture all of this additional information close to where you will need it next.

The following section of the workbook is about the practical drafting of the scope document. You will now move from research into creating the website you want, first by drawing up a sitemap.

During these stages, you will want to refer to all of your learnings often, and the affinity diagrams should help with that. On the following pages record any other notes that you have made, during this process, to keep them top of mind.

What types of notes did you keep?

- Possible content topics
- Key design observations
- Important late observations

The type doesn't matter but if you find you've got information written outside of the book or in earlier chapters

----

_____

_____

_____

_____

_____

_____

_____

_____

_____

_____

_____

_____

SITEMAPPING

➤ Sitemap Your Website

In this section, we'll walk through the steps of creating a visual sitemap for your new site.

The term "Sitemap" can confuse people because there are several different meanings to a website site map.

1. 1. A technical sitemap is a file, or series of files, that are used to guide a search engine, or other bots, for their crawl of a site.

2. 2. A sitemap page, displayed on a website, shows all the pages, or key pages of the site to users so that they can navigate the site from a single list of page links.

3. 3. The sitemap I will refer to is a **Visual Sitemap** that serves the purpose of helping to construct the site architecture.

The sitemap we will build serves several purposes:

- To provide a visual plan of the website
- To help in constructing informational architecture for the site
- It can assist in navigation decisions in later stages
- Create a list of all the critical pages of the site that will need to be scoped and built.

Some people can work more efficiently with a visual layout, while others prefer lists. In **The Complete Website Planning Guide**, I outline both methods. In this workbook, we are working on the visual approach.

The list format uses a simple spreadsheet, or indented numbered list, to list out the pages in a parent/child relationship.

When you prepare the final documentation, my recommendation would be to include both types of sitemap.

When you completed the previous chapter, Sorting the Data, you were also helping to construct the logical groups that will inform this part of the planning process.

As you work through the sitemap, you will see how useful those groups become in determining how to represent these issues and topics on the site. You will also know where the most logical locations for them in the site architecture will be.

You will review your affinity diagrams and other vital observations looking for topics, themes and likely content for your new site.

The steps outlined in the following pages will guide you on a method to translate the needs you've already outlined into sections of the site. Then the pages within each of those sections and any other pages that are required to complete the website.

Starting with the sitemap will give you the foundations of the overall scope. You will rarely draft it all correctly the first time you do it. It is more likely that as you complete the subsequent chapters, page scoping and wireframing, you will need to modify the sitemap

You will find that they are best completed in parallel, rather than in a linear fashion.

As an example, you might add a contact page to your sitemap. When you start to scope that page, you may realize that there is a need for three different types of form for the different types of inquiries.

Thus you would come back to the contact section in the sitemap, add in the three sub-pages and name them, then create scopes for each of them.

As you work through the sitemap, treat it as a series of drafts, that you won't finalize until after the entire scope is ready to be presented to key stakeholders.

Sitemaps are not something that you need inside industry knowledge to create. Everyone uses websites and instinctively knows when a site is easy to navigate through and those that aren't.

When the information is presented logically and has a flow to it, you know it has been well planned. Typically there's a logical information hierarchy as well as consideration of the user journey on these sites.

If you are someone that works on websites, use your experience in designing or building sites. If you don't, then think about how you use other websites to help you draw the sitemap by thinking in each instance "what happens next?"

Everything that goes into the sitemap should be a page. Don't show workflow functionality in the sitemap; you will want to record functional workflow as part of the scope.

As you consider each page you are adding to the sitemap ask yourself:

- Is this a new section and it's the Top-Level Page?
- Does it belong in an existing section, or a new section but an inner page?
- Is it the result of action on a previous page?

You will do this by repeatedly referring back to your previous observations. Work through every page you believe you need on the site.

Don't worry about navigation.

The sitemap is not about site navigation. The role of the sitemap is to show the architecture, or structure, of the website.

Navigation is a design and usability decision, informed by the sitemap and other elements of the plan, including individual scope requirements.

Information Architecture is concerned with helping users find information and complete tasks. Using this statement as a guide to your thought processes, look at how the individual pieces fit together, to achieve the main goals of the website.

- How does each item relate to others?
- Where do pieces of content or functions need to belong?

The sitemap doesn't explain functionality. It just shows the pages of the website and their relationship to each other.

For example. On a hotel booking website that has search functionality and search results you would create pages like below:

- Search Hotels Page

- Search Results Page

- Individual Hotel Page

That is enough for your sitemap. You will provide the detail about what is required when you do the functional requirements part of this planning process.

For more complex sites, often one canvas is not enough to represent the entire site. In these cases use a series of canvases to create the overall sitemap.

What that means is to break up the sitemap into multiple pages. The first page would show the top-level pages, or sections, of the site and core pages.

If for example you had a shop as part of your site and it was reasonably extensive you could color the page called 'Shop' orange. On a second page, you would then create the sitemap of the shop section only.

The top-level of this sitemap would be 'Shop Home' or similar, whereas on the first level page it would be 'Home Page'. If you color the Shop Home page orange as well, it becomes very obvious to people viewing the documents in the future, the relationship between them.

Trying to squeeze everything into one page will only make the objects so small it is almost impossible to read them. There are pages in this workbook for you to draw up your sitemap, however, long term you will want to digitize it, and we have recommended options for that.

What Does a Sitemap Look Like?

Sitemap Example 1

This example is a sitemap for a smaller Lawyers site that is predominantly an online brochure. The goal of this site might be; *offering a professional outline of services for referrals to review the business.*

It doesn't have a lot of depth and is a very simple sitemap to put together. See the notes about it in the following pages.

Sitemap Example 1

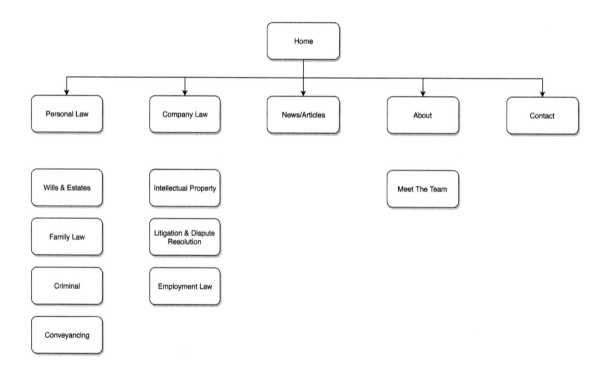

About Example 1

The sitemap on the previous page outlines the main pages of the website as well as any relevant functional pages or steps, e.g. the contact inquiry steps.

In some sitemaps, you might have essential elements of functionality that aren't a page but are part of the flow of the site. It could be a popup that shows substantial content. You should include that as if it was a page as it is an integral part of the site and ultimately behaves like a page.

If you have complex functionality happening on a series of pages, then you would be best served to create a separate workflow diagram for it. This diagram would show the steps in the process. You would link it to a page on the sitemap with a notation.

You can see in this example each page is numbered in a sequence, relating the parent and child relationship both visually and numerically.

Show every page, including groups of pages, such as in the example of the News section. While the news pages will be created dynamically and built automatically by the content management system, they are still a page. A template needs to be specified, designed, built and tested for the news articles, so it is essential to include it in the sitemap.

The same principle works on e-commerce sites. You might not list out every product, as they will likely use a template that is consistent for all products, but you would create pages for categories. Refer to example 2.

➤ Sitemap Example 2

The following example is a sitemap for an e-commerce store. Sites with shopping functionality have specific requirements, and most of the sitemap will focus on that. Each of those pages, e.g. cart, checkout, etc., still need to be mapped and specified.

Most of the pages within a shopping site are built automatically, for example, the category pages. It is advisable to list the categories you are aware of now, to accurately show the scale of the site.

You might not show every subcategory on the sitemap, and you won't show all the products. You will want to be able to consider which sections might need custom functionality or design so show enough to help everyone understand the needs.

If you only sitemap and scope one template, that is the result you will get.

As mentioned earlier, complex navigation decisions need a way to see all the relationships to help design something user-friendly.

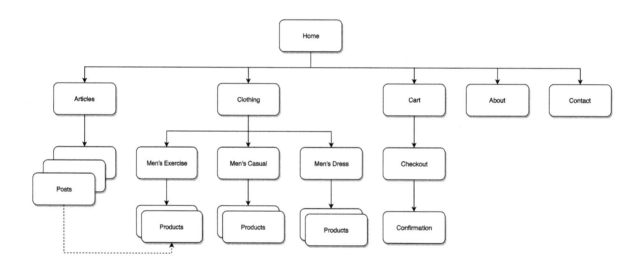

➤ About Example 2

An essential part of the sitemap for this e-commerce store is the depth of pages across the site. Not only are there a series of categories and subcategories for the products, but there's also a series of content pages in groups or sections.

While the individual products haven't been broken down with product names, the categories have been. As discussed earlier, this is the preferable way to handle such a sitemap. Err on the side of more information, not less.

At the wireframing and design stages being able to easily see the scope of the site will help that process. When you are modelling up a wireframe, you need to be able to use the context of the number of categories, which you will use within on-page and menu-based navigation.

The decisions needed to make something user-friendly are best influenced early with actual content rather than having to come back and fix something much later in the process.

While you might not have exact numbers, representing the scope of it will avoid problems later on.

➤ Starting Your Sitemap

The easiest way to start with a sitemap is often using pen and paper.

That allows you to create the skeleton quickly before committing to a digital document. I prefer this method because in most cases, I move objects around a lot as I extract more elements from the data.

Whichever method you choose to use, getting started is always done best by completing the easy and obvious pages that your site is going to have.

For many sites, there are some conventions which you will adhere to, such as:

- A 'Contact' page
- Some form of 'About' page
- 'Privacy policy'
- 'Terms and conditions'
- Etc.

Start by adding these into the sitemap.

When adding peripheral pages such as Privacy Policy I tend to put them at the bottom of the sitemap so that they can be seen and not ignored but out of the way of the main content. You can always position them more appropriately later.

If these pages were part of a 'legal' section of the site, then you would put them in that grouping.

Draw in Home Page, About Us, Contact Us, as a start.

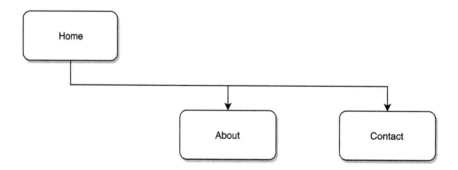

➤ Next Steps

Now we want to start creating areas of the site relating to the core needs we have for it. Typically I will include key elements that I know will be needed. If it has a shopping component, then I know there's a shop or store page, a cart, and checkout. I'll add these to one side before I tackle the products.

For a site with content and services, I try to cover all the static individual content areas, so they are on the sitemap, perhaps to the side, and then tackle some of the content area groups.

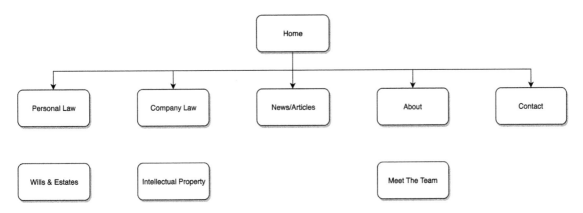

In the diagram, we've added in additional services pages, which address groups of the content we've determined we need.

At this point, we are just handling the top level, and you will expand them out as you progress.

.

➤ Completing the Sitemap

To complete the sitemap, you will continue to work through systematically adding new pages.

You may find it useful to have pre-prepared your existing website's sitemap to compare areas as you map them out. Sometimes that can influence you into copying what you already have.

Referring back to the existing one at least when you complete the sitemap will help you double-check you haven't omitted something important.

Continually work your way through the information you gathered and use the following points to help you in placing pages on the sitemap:

- How useful to your audience is it?
- For answering questions, locate the best possible (most relevant) place to do that
- Will it need more information or less - i.e. can you include multiple points on one page or do they need individual pages?
- Is it supporting content to provide trust, or is it standalone content?
- Is it for search optimization, or is it part of a workflow?
- Is it a landing page in its own right or is it part of a content section, e.g. news?

Content needs:

You will need to look at the deficiencies that you have found in the information you currently are providing. In the example of our Legal website, we identified there were some trust concerns regarding lawyers. You will need to decide the best way to present and provide that information.

One method might be to create a section called 'Why should you trust a lawyer?'

You would want this section to be specifically for a set group of people. Within this area of the site, you might determine it only needs one page of content or that it is a top-level section for 4-10 pieces of content.

You need to be mindful of its relationship to problems you identified and who it is targeting. You wouldn't want this content in the middle of pages targeting existing clients, or more advanced people, who are trying to learn more about your processes.

You might subtly link to this 'Trust' page on several of the service pages. That can be done within content rather than an overt block or call to action. You probably wouldn't just put it into a resources section without context.

Alternatively, you might use small snippets of trust-building content highlighting specific benefits from using lawyers and some testimonials that reinforce these within other pages.

You might choose to call a single page something less confrontational, such as 'The ways lawyers protect you with a will.' That is a page that might live in your news or articles section or under the Wills section.

As you can see in the above examples, the process of completing a sitemap coincides with decisions relating to the functionality of the pages and potentially wireframes.

While you can handle these stages independently, it can create problems if you have different people work on them. There is a cross-over between the steps that can be lost when one person or group doesn't address them together.

Using past data

It is critical that you not only look at content needs in your sitemap but also the information you learned in your research relating to the usability of the site.

You may have discovered there's an existing problem with how people need to navigate through multiple pages to find the buying page for a product or product group.

In this instance, you will need to consider the pathway to core products, and see if the natural groupings are working.

In the example of a wine site, having generic pathways through Wine > Reds > {Varietal} etc. means you are making your users work hard to find what they want.

While you need a basic structure for first-time users and simple information architecture, you might also want a series of pages for 'types of wine lovers'. e.g. Hard Chards, for Chardonnay-loving people.

Having a page focused on high-value Chardonnay with additional explanations could be something that drives better user experience. Of course, you'd then make several pages for key categories as well.

Alternatively, you might try to drive existing customers to log in to the site and display recommendations, and previous orders for them, which will speed up their purchase path.

You might discover that users are bouncing from a particular page far too often. That could be simply because there wasn't enough other related content on the page or it was a very generic template.

Thus the use of past data can influence more than just who to target; it will help make better overall structure decisions.

Create pages for all such new content in your sitemap.

Using research

Sometimes we follow the way competitors do things without any context of how their site performs. If you can't see their sales data or their analytics, your assumption they are 'getting it right' may be way off base.

We all follow web standards as best we can; however, the purpose of planning your site is to do what is best for your business. You should be looking for opportunities to do the very best you can with the information you have about your business.

Instead of having four service pages that everyone is pushed through, your data might suggest a better way. Your persona building might have identified your Marketing Agency doesn't provide an SEO package for different-sized businesses. You only have a one-size-fits-all page.

What you have is a very mixed audience where a small business has a very marketing mature owner, with a much bigger budget than some other personas.

So, in this case, you might build out pages that cater to their needs, rather than services. For example, a page "Who are you?" where you outline choices for them to choose such as DIY, Help my agency, I'm a marketing manager etc.

Each one of these links to a page where you highlight what you have learned their concerns and issues are. You can then introduce them to the types of services that match these issues, and case studies or examples of how you've solved these examples in the past.

Reviewing all the information you have at hand, and all the research you completed, now becomes very powerful. You create a more comprehensive arrangement of pages for your website to help your users.

Your design team will now have much more to work with to help create better navigational paths through your site with end goals in mind. You will end up with a better selection of services suited to the right types of people and as such, more likely to convert.

All of this helps you achieve the goals you set at the beginning.

In each of these cases, you need to step back and look at everything you have learned and not just map out a traditional set of pages.

Put yourself into the mindset of your users (using your personas) to get the context of how they would think on a particular page. As they move through your site, what pages or options will be required to serve them best?

Don't look at the content you have already when you build this map! You want to create the sitemap that meets the needs you have identified.

Worry about how to create content for it later.

It is rare when doing all this work that your existing content will fulfil all the new requirements.

Throughout this process and the subsequent steps don't just refer back to your research but also keep your website goals close at hand. While everything we do we want focused on our users, we still are here to achieve the goals for our business.

Also, note there is no numbering used on the example sitemaps at this stage. I don't add numbers until I have finalized the first primary draft and am moving into the scoping phase. That's because typically I make many changes in the early stages.

Go ahead now and finish off your sitemap.

SCOPING

The Website Scope

This part of your website plan process is about documenting the role each page on the site has.

You have created a sitemap that outlines all of the pages and key elements of the site. Each page on the sitemap now has to be explained in detail.

This detail will include the goals of the page, all the functionality required and what content you will need for it.

As in the site mapping stage, you should have your goals in front of you while working through this process.

The whole purpose of this process is to make sure that you create the best possible website for your organization. The site needs to have clear goals; each page and piece of content should be fulfilling a role.

In **The Complete Website Planning Guide** process, we require you to allocate a goal to every page of the site. That is deliberate.

No page or process should exist on your website unless it has a purpose. You need to be clear what that purpose is. The goal for each page can be straightforward, but it needs to have one.

Each small goal should be adding up to the main site goals.

When you are working through the template completing details for pages, it might seem to be superfluous; some pages have little information needed other than the obvious. E.g. it's a contact page.

Give each page your full focus when you are scoping so that you don't miss valuable opportunities. We'll provide examples of goals for you to help you set them.

When working on sites, it is common for me to be considering the wireframes of pages at the same time as writing their scope. That's because when I am drafting layouts for them, I am forced to look at the way the page will help deliver the goal.

If you are comfortable with the basics of wireframing I recommend you consider that as well. If not, understand that when you do get to the wireframing stage, you will most likely want to change parts of these scopes.

I recommend that you do an initial draft of the scope, working through all the core pages, as outlined on the next set of pages, then start drafting wireframes. While you wireframe each page, you will be referring to the page scope.

As inspiration and ideas on how to implement the page come to the fore, adjust the scope accordingly. You shouldn't be modifying the goal for the page unless you didn't get that right on the first run through. You should, however, see opportunities to implement functionality that will help achieve these goals.

On a particular page, you might determine that to achieve one of the site goals, you should insert a special promotional block or selector element. It was not apparent when scoping that page it was needed, but with this decision in the wireframe, you will add the specifications for it into the page scope.

Information from your Must-Haves section will get inserted into the page scopes. There was likely feedback from internal stakeholders earlier in your research that gave you requests which didn't fit anywhere else. Now you can see where to use it. E.g. on a contact page we need to have a choice of inquiry type for support etc.

This level of detail belongs in the page scope.

You might have advised to implement Schema markup for a particular type of content. While writing the scope for those pages, you will include that information into the page scope.

The scope pages are used to record the absolute requirements page by page. In a development process, summaries, broad explanations and other forms of information get lost in the development of the project. When you insert specifics into a page-by-page guide, you remove the reliance on any one individual to remember what is required. That allows every person working on the website to be able to see what you need on each page.

You don't need to be very technical to complete the scoping phase. It can be confused with a Technical Requirements document.

While it is correct, you will need to be able to gather technical information to include in it; you will write most of the requirements in plain language.

The theory is that the plan is independent of the solution. **Your Website Planning Guide** will outline what is required and why. It will be in a language that doesn't specify how anyone will implement it.

This guide is then given to technical teams to interpret how it will be implemented and present options back to the team running the project.

That is how you ensure you get the right solution, and you get the results you planned.

Instead of having technical people dictating their solution and making your site fit into the solution, you advise what you need. It is then their job to sell you on how their solution will deliver it.

You provide the blueprints of the destination and the critical pieces needed to make sure it creates the right results for your business. Then you hire people to help bring that to fruition.

Scope Template

This is the Scoping Template we use for our projects

#	Page	
	URL	

Page Summary

Page Goal

Page Functionality

Media / Copy Requirements

Amendments

Date	Who	What

Filling In The Template

Page Number

The Page Number is the number used in the sitemap. For example, the Home Page is always 1.0.

You will find it best to leave the numbering until the very end to save you adjusting the order of pages. Where pages live in a hierarchical tree, you would name the child pages under the parent. E.g. if Services is 2.0, then the list of services might be:

2.0 Services

> *2.1 House Cleaning*
>
> *2.2 Office Cleaning*
>
> *2.3 Forensic Cleaning*

You will extrapolate this out if there are further branches. E.g.

2.0 Services

> 2.1 House Cleaning
>
> > *2.1.1 Inside Cleaning*
> >
> > *2.1.2 Exterior Cleaning*
> >
> > *2.1.3 Special Occasion Cleaning*

Name

The name of how you will refer to the page. E.g. House Cleaning

URL

The URL you will use on the site.

You might require input from other team members, for example, those working on your Search Engine Optimization to complete these.

If you are unsure initially on the URL structure that you will use, then skip it and come back to it before you complete the final parts of the plan.

Often it won't be until you finalize your sitemap that you want someone to lock down on the URLs, as the sitemap will influence the URLs.

Write the URLs as relative URLs. E.g. /services/ or /services/house-cleaning/

#	Page	
	URL	

Page Goal

Few website briefs detail individual goals for every page. That is wrong. As mentioned earlier if a page has no goal for your site, then you shouldn't include it.

You should not just transplant the site-wide goals onto a page either. Site-wide goals are your business objectives for the site. Everything about the website should be architected to achieve them.

These site-wide goals would rarely be laid out onto any one page. Achieving those goals will occur through you achieving smaller goals throughout the site.

Each page is a stepping stone towards the larger goals.

While the goal of an e-commerce site might be to increase sales to a specific amount, the way you achieve this is through growing sales one by one.

In reality, the only page that guarantees a sale is the confirmation page after checkout. All other pages should be working towards that goal. The checkout page goal won't be to increase sales either.

The goal of the checkout page is likely to be similar to;

"Ensure the purchaser can complete their sale in under 7 seconds and reduce abandonment to less than 1 in 10."

Making this goal-specific and measurable, changes the way, you look at this page.

If you have a secondary goal to build a newsletter list then it won't even be considered on this page.

With our goal to speed up the checkout and reduce abandonment, we are likely not to add a checkbox relating to our newsletter to the checkout process. This friction could impact our goal. So we might add promotion of our newsletter into the post-sale email. It is likely to be much more effective and still supports both primary page goals and secondary site goals.

This level of focus on individual page goals will help you drive the results you want.

Page Goal
Page Functionality
Media / Copy Requirements

Page Summary

The summary should be used to outline the role of the page. Even if the purpose of the page is obvious, you should always put it in writing.

E.g. To display information about our company (About Us)

Page Functionality

This section of the template is where you will need to describe in as much detail as possible all functionality that is part of this page.

You do not need to include navigation, headers and footers on individual pages; you will handle these separately.

You only want to document functionality for what happens on this page. Using bullet points is helpful to make it easier for development teams to be able to read the requirements easily. Understanding how others will use the details helps you lay it out in a way that will ensure nothing gets forgotten.

Do **NOT** try to limit the functionality to the size of the template. Use as much space as you need. If a page needs to take up three printed pages in length, then that's what you do. Ultimately you will need to move all of this workbook content into a digital version, and page length does not matter.

What matters is that you describe the highest amount of useful detail as possible per page to ensure you are documenting the exact requirements.

When you document all of your requirements, then you will no longer suffer from one of the most common problems in website development. Not getting what you thought you were going to get.

Page Functionality		

Media / Copy Requirements		

Amendments		
Date	**Who**	**What**

The functionality section outlines in detail exactly what each page does. Anyone who will be working on your website has every opportunity to clarify what each page needs to do. There's no reason then not to build exactly what you have asked for.

How to detail the functionality?

1. Be specific - name and explain each item in detail.

2. If you are naming a field for a form, write out the name of the field and what type of input will be required (e.g. text or international phone number). Also, advise whether it is mandatory or not.

3. Over-detail, don't under-detail. Assume that the reader won't have your level of understanding about the business or technology.

4. Include Calls to actions (CTA). e.g. CTA to sign-up form. Note the text for the CTA doesn't need to be specified at this point. If one CTA is more important than another, explain that and the reason why.

5. Outline the types of diagrams or images that might be required. E.g. Graph showing example improvement in client's business from this service

This is a time-consuming process. It requires you to cross-reference the previous sections of this workbook constantly. The effort is well worth it.

You need to be reviewing what was previously written for the overall goals and understand what part of the journey a user will be on when they are on any individual page.

How can this page contribute to the bigger goal? How can you make the stepping-stones all link up logically?

You will need to include all of the Must-Have items within individual pages where relevant.

You will refer to all of your research. For example, where you learned about poor bounce rates, you need to address it within the page scope.

Where you watched users struggle with poor usability in user testing videos, you need to outline the fixes or the need to fix it.

Where you noticed poor click patterns or scrolling of content, you need to include descriptions and functionality that drive better results.

Some examples:

- Include a CTA to scroll lower on the page

- Insert an illustration that hooks the reader to explore further

- Insert a specific testimonial here to increase trust high enough to make the page stickier

Be careful that you do not use competing CTAs. That is a common mistake on websites. It is where each CTA is given as much importance as another on the same page. It makes for a poor user experience and typically means the page doesn't have a clear goal.

Media/Copy Requirements

In this section of the template, you will be listing out the content needs for the page.

Each section of the template provides information for different people in the design and development phase.

In this section, you are enabling the content production team to work from specifics to them without them having to dig through all of the scope documents. Leaving them to self-direct what is required can only hamper the project management process.

Completing this section after you have outlined the functionality will enable you to list out items such as:

- CTA text for primary CTA
- CTA text for secondary link CTA

You will list out each section of content requirements, including any media elements: E.g.:

- Video showing customer interview
- Introductory text content to explain the page purpose
- Page content
- Hero image
- Icon for heading 2

This section is a list of requirements; it isn't outlining the actual copy itself unless you need to guide its purpose.

Like all the other parts of the scope, you will be cross-referencing your requirements to make sure all topics are covered.

Later, when you produce the final document which encompasses the entire scope for your project, you will use the content requirements portion to create your master content checklist.

Amendments

This section of the plan template is for use in the actual project management process. Despite all the planning effort, situations will arise during the build where change will be needed. It might come from technical issues, changes to the business needs or other triggers.

An error might have been made without observation and is corrected during the design and build phase.

When this happens, the change should be noted in the relevant section.

This informs the testing teams of the actual requirements and will be used in the final acceptance testing by the client.

Completing the Scoping

Work through every page on the site using as much detail as possible.

When you have specific technical sections of the site or processes that do not fit into the typical page template, then you will need to detail them differently.

Using:

6. The functional specification template

7. Flow charts.

You can use any format that works. The critical element is to have clear documentation that explains your requirements.

Examples include specific dynamic pieces of functionality or custom notification processes that are triggered by actions on an individual page.

If a site visitor purchases a product using the step-by-step checkout process, you will use the templates we've already covered.

If post purchase, there are a series of steps needed to support your business goals such as notification SMS messages or emails, then these need to be detailed as well.

You should be working on the premise that if it isn't in this document set, then it won't be paid for or built. So if it is needed, it must be explained in detail.

If you don't have enough pages in this workbook for the size of your website, please download the templates from **https://ireck.in/wpgwork** and print additional copies.

Page Functionality		

Media / Copy Requirements		

Amendments		
Date	**Who**	**What**

WIREFRAMING

➤ Wireframe Your Pages

Wireframing is the vital link between the scope and all your data and the design. Websites without plans often start with the design and work backwards.

Wireframes are a critical step allowing all stakeholders to have input into the way you want the site layout designed. Wireframes are especially important in gaining approval from multiple decision-makers before spending time and money on the designs and prototypes.

Design decisions are often as much about what not to include as what is. Usability issues can be considered much more efficiently in a wireframe process, without the decisions that will get made around the look.

Wireframes are NOT visual designs; they do NOT typically include images, color choices or illustrations. They do often include some content elements, such as headings, calls to action or portions of actual written text.

You will slow down the wireframing process if you include color, images and other rich media into your wireframes. More importantly, you will find yourself making critical design decisions during the phase when you should be only concerned about functionality and needs.

Make all of your design decisions at the design phase. If you want to spend three hours debating a color do it then, not at this stage. When you mix the steps, projects can become deadlocked as design influence ends up altering functionality decisions.

The wireframe is deliberately meant to be a bare-bones skeletal layout of a page. It should allow critical thought about the usability, how to translate the functionality into the page, and how different content media will fit into the page.

It is the surest pathway to making sure you get the results you want, not just the color object you want. The purpose of **The Complete Website Planning Guide** is to allow you to control your website results.

When you write your scope for each page in many cases, you would have generic statements about content and specific comments about the vital functionality.

Using wireframes, you will see how this will play out on a page and learn if you have missed anything important, or if you can remove elements.

While the process of creating the wireframes can be an additional phase to scoping the pages, it is often done at the same time. Bouncing between the two steps as they inform your choices for the page.

If you didn't work in this way when you did your scope, make sure as you wireframe each page you look to find any flaws in what you scoped. Look at whether you've included items that aren't necessary or discover those you missed.

Update the scope and make sure the wireframes include everything from the scope. We have added some pages in this workbook to draw wireframes. For most websites it will not be enough, so you will want to download the template from our resources: **https://ireck.in/wpgwork**

When wireframing on paper, you will make many revisions. Start with a pencil and eraser until you are confident about what you will need. Don't be afraid to leave gaps if you are unsure about a part of a page, and come back to it as you work. Create a box for that element and title it so that everyone knows what will go into the page at that point.

Your goal is to place the correct items in the best order for the goals you set for the page you are wireframing.

Some people feel that they need to be a designer to do a wireframe. That is understandable, especially if you are referring to hi-fidelity wireframes. There's no need to be at that level.

If you have been working through the scope as instructed in this workbook, you will be able to see how elements will get placed onto a page. Don't get confused that you need to create anything more than a series of boxes with labels.

For example; if you've decided that you want your users to see three service options as a priority on a particular page. You will then need to make sure they are high on the page and above 'the fold'. So draw three equal boxes in place on the wireframe.

The page may only have Navigation, Top of Page, 3 Selection Options, Some content, Footer on it.

For your wireframing, this is all that is needed. If you are more experienced, you might add a lot more detail. When you engage a designer, you will know why you have this level of placement, and they can then consider how to interpret that.

Do not assume that all designers are necessarily experts in usability and needs analysis. Your designer might be skilled but relatively new to web design. They will be more likely to recommend what they are comfortable with and not necessarily what you need. When you are more explicit, you force them to stretch themselves into coming up with suitable design decisions.

An experienced designer won't be put out by your wireframes; it makes their job easier as you have done a lot of the thinking allowing them to be even more creative with their time.

➤ Wirefame For Devices

You will be required to create two wireframes per page.

- 1 x Mobile wireframe and,
- 1 x Desktop wireframe.

It is a critical step, particularly in a world where Mobile use has overtaken the use of Desktop.

Typically your clients and key stakeholders will be most interested and spend more time in the Desktop view of your design. That's where you will get the most feedback and discussion.

When you wireframe the two alongside each other, you can see why the mobile view is very linear and has less room for creative expression. The Desktop is also the traditional view that business users typically see. They are comfortable with it, and that is the view they usually associate with website design.

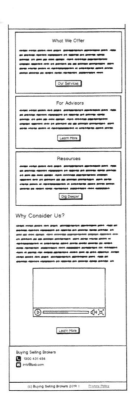

A mobile wireframe

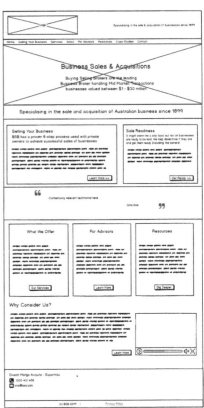

A desktop wireframe

Your role is to make sure you apply as much thought to both views and create wireframes expressing clearly how the pages will work in both sizings. Some teams will also do a tablet resolution wireframe as well. If you have complex interactive pages that require special consideration, then you can also create a mid-size wireframe for this purpose.

Key Components of Wireframing

You need not be concerned about your technical or design capabilities when creating wireframes. As already mentioned wireframes are simply outlines of what the page will contain using line drawings.

Below are some examples of the types of objects you might draw into your pages as a guide to get you started.

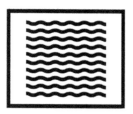

A block of text. You do not need to place the actual text into the wireframe, the use of squiggly lines, or *lorem ipsum* text is standard.

Headings. Wherever possible put in a title that is reflective of the actual text you will use. It will be checked and corrected by your copywriters later in your build process..

Image panel. A box with diagonal lines through it to represent an image is all that's needed to show where you will use visual imagery.

Buttons. Buttons are essential calls to action and navigation steps. If you want to use a button rather than a link, then make sure to draw a button and use action text.

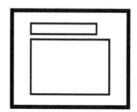

Form elements. If you need an input field or drop-down, then draw a representation of them, so it is clear this is an interactive section of the page.

Action orientated elements. If your page is using objects that change behavior, e.g. an accordion or carousel, then you will need to draw indicators for each state. I.e. open and closed, so that it is clear what the wireframe represents.

Video. You will need a video panel ideally with a play button on it so it is clear this is a video and not an image.

Audio. If you want to display an audio element, then you will need an object with a play icon that symbolizes audio only.

Navigation. Menu bar or bars need to be drawn on the site.

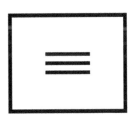

Mobile navigation. Mobile navigation is different from desktop/tablet navigation commonly associated with hamburger menu options.

Navigation drop down menus. Being able to display the open state of a menu is important for both design and navigation understanding.

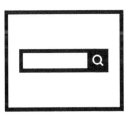

Other page elements. There are many items such as share icons, search bars and others that you will need to use to wireframe your pages correctly.

➤ Mobile First

Most web design and development is now heavily influenced by mobile and other device usage. What used to be exclusively a desktop environment is now predominantly mobile. In truth, it is a multi-sized and multi-device environment that is continually changing.

Many stakeholders will fall back to wanting to see and approve only desktop-sized designs and prototypes. It is vital in the planning process that you recognize the importance of mobile requirements, and you should be placing them first in all of your planning decisions.

In wireframing, it means twice the work for you. You need to draw up both mobile and desktop versions of the pages.

You will also need to note in the specifics of the scoping documents about variations on pages between devices.

It is true you might not know the full technical ramifications of your plans. It is another benefit of your Complete Website Plan. It will allow the teams presenting to you about your project to identify any potential issues they see before you start the project.

When needing to make compromises on your project, it is better to do it within the context of a full scope than in a piecemeal fashion.

One of the reasons people prefer desktop designs and layouts is because they can be much more visually appealing. There is a much larger canvas to create impressive visual elements, and to add in titillating details that appeal to the human desire for "cool things".

Designers like them too, as there is a lot more space to show off their abilities.

Your job in planning the site is not to determine the final visual result upfront.

Your job is to ensure you meet the goals and objectives for this website investment.

Traditionally the approach was to have desktop sites containing everything and then to make a poor cousin on mobile. It was partly driven by the limitations of early mobile devices and browsers and also speed issues.

The reasoning behind it left many users with terrible mobile experiences, which frustrated them and didn't help make the mobile web a practical place to be.

You should plan your site based on actual needs and plan to deliver a positive, useful experience to the people who will use it. Work on the premise that if it isn't needed on mobile, then it has no purpose on desktop either.

Use the mobile planning process to clarify how much you need to put onto each page and what purpose it serves.

Will a particular element that will be hardly noticeable on mobile do anything that generates a positive ROI on desktop, or is it there simply to fill in space on the larger screen size? Are you copying another site by wanting that element on your desktop design?

Where to Start

Many people will quite naturally start with the home page and then work their way down through the hierarchy from the sitemap when wireframing.

This approach makes a lot of sense; you start with the head page and formulate the overall shape. You then proceed through each of the pages until completion.

An alternate approach and one that I prefer is where you start further down the tree and work your way backwards.

By working on the key sections of the site, followed by the peripheral pages, you make your critical decisions about the importance of content within each area of the website. When you get to the home page, it almost draws itself as it is responding to what its role is within the context of all pages.

You will have a much better sense of the calls to action, interactive elements and the steps that you have been laying out for users through your site.

When you get to top-level landing pages and the home page, it should be much easier at that point to determine how the essential elements will be laid out. What will sit highest on the page? How will other things follow? Where do you want the user to focus and how will that be achieved?

Assuming that you are working through the Scoping and Wireframing steps in tandem, as previously suggested, this also assists you in clarifying all of the functionality of the most important pages.

Whichever method you choose to complete this step, make sure you draw wireframes for all pages. The combination of wireframes and functional scope tell the complete story of each page.

➤ From Scope to Wireframe

Translating your scope into a working wireframe

The wireframe is a layout guide to the scope you prepared earlier. As noted these two steps work hand in hand with each other. The scope will always have more detail in it than the wireframe.

Functional elements will be described in detail in the scope of the page whereas the wireframe is showing where items are laid out. We will walk you through some guides on moving from the written scope to a useful wireframe.

Page goal

When you start the page wireframe the foremost thing to remember is the page goal. Revisit the goal, ensure it's clear and specific. ,

Now consider what will be the best way of achieving that goal. Starting with the mobile view, where on the page will the progression to this goal occur?

Think about what steps the user will need to walk through to achieve this goal.

It might be a page that is a gateway to additional content, the goal being to help the user choose the right option out of four options. Then you need to ensure that the way the options are laid out doesn't influence the result unless that's what you want. e.g. if you make one of the choices more prominent then more people are likely to click on it.

In the desktop view, you have more freedom to lay four items across the width of the page so that they all get immediate visibility. The mobile experience is very different, so if you applied the same layout concept stacked, there would be an automatic priority system used. More people will see the top one and as such, is likely to get more clicks.

That may be something you want, in which case that's a deliberate layout decision; if not you need to reimagine a better way to show all four options.

Perhaps it's four links which when clicked/touched scroll the user down the page (anchor links) or the use of accordions etc.

Focus on the goal first before laying anything onto the page, then position your primary goal where you want to see it.

Adding functionality

The first step in any wireframe is to make sure you've considered and, in theory placed the key elements of your page goal into the layout.

Next you need to work through all the other functionality that you listed in your scope. As you construct the page you may need to amend your scope.

For example, if you realize that you need to have some introductory copy to guide the user on using the functionality, you would need to add that to the scope sheet for this page.

If you discover that something you listed as necessary isn't actually required on this page once you are able to visualize it better, then likewise you would remove it from the scoping sheet.

Nothing is fixed at this stage; if you place an element into your wireframe that you need to rearrange then do so. Using pencil and an eraser if you are doing your wireframing on paper is ideal.

This is a workbook, and as such should reflect your workings.

Work your way down the wireframe. Due to space limitations in a workbook of this size the actual length of the wireframe isn't tall enough for one whole page, on our templates we have 3 columns. The arrows represent the continuation of the screen, from the bottom of the first column to the second etc.

Using the example elements we showed on the earlier pages you should be able to fill in enough to allow everyone involved to conceptualize the page and its functionality.

Make notes on objects or beside them to clarify them so that anyone viewing the wireframe can understand the page and what its purpose is.

The relationship between the scope that has the additional detail and the wireframe should be transparent

When you are comfortable with your initial mobile wireframe move on to the next stage.

Create the desktop version

Now that you have completed the mobile version, you should find this step much easier to complete. Much of the critical thinking has already been completed.

For simple content pages, the work here is straightforward.

On most pages, you will need to review each of the objects you used on mobile and think about the role and purpose you chose for them.

You will now need to translate this purpose to the larger format of the desktop.

It is common that people then feel challenged in working with the bigger size and want to add more items into it.

Remember if something has no purpose on mobile or smaller screens, then you need to think about why you need it on desktop. Are you using a feeling of discomfort or conformity to traditional desktop design concepts in guiding changes you want to make?

Everything should have a purpose. If it doesn't make sense to have a full-screen image on mobile, and less than 50% of your users will be on a desktop, do you need it?

Mapping the new size

Move each of your objects on to the larger format.

Elements need to still have a relationship to the mobile version. Items that stack on mobile can be left or right of their partner elements on desktop. However an element 2 objects away on mobile can't be next to the first object on desktop.

While this is a little piece of technical advice it is useful to understand it.

An object on desktop could take up ⅔ of the screen width and the object next to it could take up ⅓ while on desktop their width is the same. That will work, the wider one will become taller on mobile.

Checking the flow

Once you have both wireframes first draft drawn up you then need to double check the flow of both pages.

Start with mobile and make sure it works well. To do this you need to consider the actual user viewing the screen on their device.

Think about screen sizes on mobile, what will be visible on the first screen and what the flow will be like when you scroll or touch elements.

Proportions matter in wireframes, as they reflect your vision of how these screens should work for users.

When the design team reviews these wireframe they should be able to understand the spatial relationships between elements. Your consideration of these elements will help you get the right result.

You don't need to fully understand how they design; you need to think about how a screen will work. Get your phone out, or use a screen-sized piece of paper and place different sized cut-outs on it. Think about what you are trying to achieve.

If your object is an image and fills the whole screen, then the user has to wait for that to load and then understand they need to scroll to see below it. Is this the behavior you want to have?

Consider the competition between elements as you scroll down the screen; if the bottom of one object has a large button and within the next panel you see there's a competing button, think about your goals, and consider the best way to tackle this. Should one be a text link to be of lesser importance etc.

Work your way through the entire mobile wireframe. Then when happy with it make any changes necessary to the desktop version and review the flow of the desktop page.

Consider positioning, what should be to the left of a row, then the middle and right.

Consider the calls to action on a bigger screen and competition between elements.

Think about the sizing and the way particular elements will create focal points for users. Images or videos and large headings will stand out differently on desktop than mobile.

Each of these considerations impacts a good page layout.

Your design team can solve some issues with color and other design tools, so if you can't come up with a resolution leave the design of the objects to solve the problem but notate that issue on the wireframe or as added notes in the scoping sheet.

➤ Wireframe Every Page

Work through every page in your scope and create mobile and desktop wireframes for each.

Remember to use workflow charts or functionality maps for more complex functionality.

Give each one the same level of treatment as your initial one, focusing first on the primary goal of the page, and then any secondary objectives.

Think about what types of content and functional elements will help serve those goals. Are there other items that will be required? As an example, perhaps to help achieve the goal of a sale or inquiry, you need to build trust on the page. Thus you might need to include a review or testimonial content reinforcing your security and privacy.

Work through all the pages, considering key landing pages from the pages you have designed underneath them. How will you connect them and help users relate to the flow you are creating?

When you need additional templates for this, we have templates you can download from here: **https://ireck.in/wpgwork**

➤ Wireframe the Home Page

Now that you have completed the wireframes for the rest of your site, it is time to complete the task by wireframing the home page.

Through the entire process, you have been focusing on individual page goals, functionality and requirements, and understanding the needs of the audience you are seeking to serve.

The home page should be the gateway to assisting those goals.

Things to remember:

- Not every visitor to your site sees your home page as his or her first page.
- The home page doesn't need to answer every question about your site, only the ones you have chosen for it.
- Don't overload the home page. Remember what are the top two to three goals for this page? Focus on them.

A common mistake is to undo all the hard work that you've done to this point and make the home page cover more topics than it needs to.

A home page is a gateway page. It should reinforce to the visitor they have landed on the right site, and help them dig deeper into the likely areas they want to find. At this point, you have little information about what they want.

If someone lands on a category-landing page, you know what they were searching for when they arrived there. It is much clearer at that point about their intent.

Wireframe Templates

Mobile:_____

Mobile:_____

Desktop:_____

Mobile:_____

Desktop:_____

Mobile:_____

Desktop:_____

Mobile:_____

Desktop:_____

Mobile:_____

Desktop:_____

CONTENT

➤ Planning Your Content

The bulk of the website will be made up of content. Most of the things a visitor to your site will see will be content. While they will have feelings about the layout of the site and the flow what they will mostly see will be the images and words.

That is why a common phrase is "Content is King". Whether King is the right term or not, the importance of content to the site cannot be understated.

Hopefully, by this stage, you will instinctively realize this based on how much research you conducted and the way you structure the site.

In the earlier steps, including the affinity diagrams and site mapping, you were laying the groundwork for the content to come.

The page content isn't just about the body copy, though. All elements on the pages contain content, including text and images, for example.

When considering the content for the site, you need to maintain a clear goal-orientated focus. You need to make conscious choices as to how much content, what type of content, and how you will use the content.

The H1 (or primary) headline is the very first piece of content on the page. Whether or not a secondary headline or a paragraph follow it will be determined by the purpose of the page and how the content will help fulfil that.

There are numerous types of content and uses depending on whether the page is a sales letter style, a brochure or specification sheet, a series of helpful hints etc.

Each type of page will have its own requirements, including the types of images, number of images and number of words.

You need to list out each requirement per page into a master list, as well as individual briefing lists as required.

In **The Complete Website Planning Guide**, I outlined the Master Content Requirement document. The following sections will guide you through what is required to complete this fully and how you will then provide this information to the relevant content producers.

➤ Scoping Page Content

This stage requires you to revisit the scoping sheets once again. You will also revisit the wireframes. It might seem repetitive to go back through the same pages several times; however, each pass over these items allows you to refine your work.

It is easy to miss something important because of process fatigue, and revisiting the sheets and wireframes helps you to guarantee you have covered everything.

The example below is the bottom section of the scoping sheet.

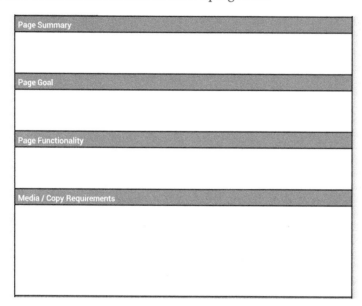

When you created the sheets earlier, you put in detail about the content, as to what is required. E.g. Images for page, Call to action text for the button.

While this sufficed in the early stages, it won't be enough for your copy production team. Similar to the way we want to control the result of the design and development, leaving the content creation to others without guidance doesn't guarantee you the best results.

Copywriters, like all people in your future development team, can only be as good as the information they are given to work with.

A quality copywriter will pepper you with questions and information requests when commissioned to work on your project.

The plan you have been building will give them the structure they require to be able to quote your project, both in time and costs.

You will need to provide them with additional information about your products and services outside of what will be in this plan. The detail in your Website Plan gives them the blueprints of what they need to prepare and removes ambiguity about your needs.

➤ Get Specific

The information in the scoping sheets now needs to get much more specific.

You need to add in the goal and purpose of the content. You are guiding the copy teams on what your expectations are. Here are some examples:

Page heading	H1 heading focused on primary need of 'Security'
Page heading	H1 heading that agitates the problem, and leads to the secondary heading
H2 heading	Subheading to hint at the possible solution
Introductory Paragraph	Due to the technical nature of the content below, this paragraph should confirm in simpler text the user is on the right page and inform them what is below
Hero Image	Hero image: Should show a café type setting with the server in focus, customers a little off screen or out of focus. Is about subtle service message
Video	Video no more than 45 seconds with a customer explaining their positive support experience.
Page Content	The body content on this page needs to highlight the key reasons this service answers the questions outlined in our product research doc.
Content Images	Due to the size of the content we want to insert images every third to fourth paragraph to break up the content and to demonstrate the core features in the content.

As you can see, each element is different and has a different reason for being on the page. Now that you have to justify each page element and the content needed, it forces to you evaluate whether you need it or not.

For example, consider the last item in the table above. Your reaction might be to think about whether the content needs to be so long. When you thoroughly review each item in your page scope, you can reflect on its purpose and role.

In this example, it might be that the technical nature of the document requires it to be long-form, and as such, the request to add images will help to break up the content.

It will also guide the copywriter into considering the issue of length as well. They can consider using breaks in the content, such as subheadings or bullets that will make the content more easily read on screen.

Work through the next sections of the workbook before you go back and reprocess the scope sheets.

As you rework each sheet, you can fill out the master content requirements document at the same time.

Content Requirements Document List

The scoping sheets and wireframes will be provided to the content producers and will help guide them in producing all of the content elements you need.

The content requirements document is a project management tool that helps you and any production teams manage the amount of content required.

Given how many elements exist on any given page it can become very easy to lose sight of one individual piece, which is why this type of document will help you twofold in the next phases.

1. In getting accurate quotes and timelines for the content production

2. In managing the project of acquiring all the content.

You can use any document to list and track all of the content required for the site. The image on this page shows the document structure we use is, and the following pages are in this format.

There is a Google Sheet version of this template available at https://ireck.in/wpgwork.

The list for your website will be quite extensive. There are several pages in this workbook for you to start this process.

Work through several of your scope pages writing in the relevant fields, then once confident download the sheet and fill it in.

➤ List Explanation

Item: This is a number for referencing each item.

Type: In the spreadsheet, this is a set of predefined options you can select. I recommend you use a glossary of terms that make sense to your organization and keep them consistent. You can update the sheet to match your needs.

We have used:

- Body Text
- Call Out
- Excerpt
- CTA (Call to Action)
- Caption
- Image
- Video
- Misc (which can be used for anything not already covered)

Page: The page name from your sitemap / scoping sheet

Reference: The number used on your scoping sheet to identify the page. E.g. 2.1

Description: Because the detail is in the actual scope sheet this can be the simplified version of the requirement. E.g hero image, body text etc.

Status: R = Requested, D = Draft (received), F = Final (received)

THE FINAL DOCUMENT

Completing Your Website Brief

The purpose of this workbook is to help you work through the steps to creating a comprehensive plan that can be used to brief the teams going to build the site.

It isn't meant to be the final document you hand over and your workings and efforts are for your benefit.

That means you now need to digitize the brief so that it can be more readily updated and shared.

My recommendations are:

- a word processor (Word/Docs) for the bulk of the document.
- a drawing program for the sitemap (draw.io or similar)
- a drawing program for the wireframes (Balsamiq, InDesign or similar)

The following content is from the original book outlining the steps to compiling the document.

It's time to bring it all together into a brief for your project.

Compiling the documents

Now is the time to do a final check and create a document that will provide anyone quoting or working on your project with a complete picture of what you want and why you want it.

In your final brief, you are going to bring together a series of pages and documents that provide:

- the background behind the project,
- the research completed for the project,
- your goals and targets for the project, and
- all of the detail you have put into the scope pieces.

This chapter completes the core of this guide and will give you more than enough information and knowledge to proceed through the development stages.

If you have reached this stage, you should congratulate yourself. You have invested time that many others don't. You won't be someone that wonders how their project got away from them. You will be able to see a successful project through to completion.

Your Finished Brief

Keep in mind that this document will have many people who need to use it.

It is the master plan for your site, the brief for your design and development team, a guide for your content producers, an approval document for key stakeholders, and much more.

It needs to have a clear structure that anyone can follow and thereby get a comprehensive understanding of the project.

When you bring it all together your Brief/Scope should include the following items:

- Goals
- Audience Outline
- Must-have Requirements
- Research Summary
- Sitemap
- Scope document
- Wireframes
- Content Outline

1. The Introduction

This written introduction should explain to anyone reviewing the project, answers to the following questions:

- Why is this project happening?
- What expectations are there for this project?
- Are there any references to existing materials? (e.g. existing websites)
- Who are the key contacts and stakeholders from your business related to this project?

One page is probably enough to outline these points. Give an overview of the project and the process you conducted in producing this document.

2. Goals

This content should come directly from what you prepared in the Goal Setting chapter. As you went through the scoping process, you would have refined the wording and specificity of the goals.

Include them here. It is worthwhile to include a statement about goals and their importance for all concerned. For example, "That all decisions made are meant to create a purpose that achieves these goals; anything else is a distraction."

Set the guidelines upfront; then if your suppliers or team get distracted by shiny gadgets or other options, you can consistently bring them back to the question:

"How does this help us achieve our goals?"

3. Audience Outline

How much content you have in this section will depend on how in-depth you have gone in building audience personas, and how much research you have done.

It would be ideal to devote several pages here to provide top-level summaries of your audience and provide full details as part of supplementary documentation when required.

Initially, prospective agencies or design teams should only need the summary level detail, and it will help both parties get through the first round of selections.

They probably won't need to see the full detail until they have been commissioned.

If you only have one or two audience profiles and an evident history of serving them, then you might as well include them here.

4. Must-Have Requirements

In Chapter 5, you listed out any specific requirements you need this website project to have for your business.

These need to be outlined here and reference where in other scope documentation that the full detail exists. This page or two should highlight everything that needs to be included and enough information to make it meaningful.

For example, "Our existing user forum http://community.businessdomain.com will be retained and key topics will be extracted and displayed on the page in our new sitemap '12.1 Community Topics'. Full API and Feed information are provided in the scope documentation.

The existing version of this can be seen at:

http://www.domain.com/oldpage"

This summary of an item will alert everyone to enough specifics without getting bogged down in technical elements. These should be handled further in the document.

It is probably worth a note to advise everyone that the items listed in this section cannot be removed in any development decisions.

5. Research Summary

When presenting what you have learned from conducting research, you won't display everything you documented in this workbook.

Ultimately the research provided information that guided each of the scoping phases, including determining the architecture of the site, content needs, functional requirements, and design needs.

In this section, you want to detail the key lessons and messages that shone through in your research. You can provide information on how it guided the rest of this brief. The readers of the briefing document should be able to get a strong sense of why you made the decisions you did.

If there is information you don't feel best to analyze or are uncertain about, then add that as an attachment to the main document. Make a note about it and that you want it to be reviewed as part of the process.

6. Sitemap

Depending on the size of your site, you may have a one-page sitemap or multiple pages. If you used a tool like draw.io or Visio, then export them as image files or PDF pages, and include these into your website brief document.

Ensure each page of the sitemap is labelled and include text references to subpages where relevant, so readers can easily make the connections between the different maps. Check your numbering is correct and every item in the scope is included.

7. Page Scope Document

Whether you include this in your brief document or not will depend on the size and the software you used to create it.

If you used Google Sheets, you can make a Read-Only copy and share that link in this overall document. That way you won't have a bloated document to send.

If you made it in Word or Excel or similar tools, then PDF it and include it in the final documents. You need to make sure each tab / page scoped is included, and any notations are shown on each page.

8. Wireframes

You will need to export all your wireframes as images or PDF documents. If you have it all in Balsamiq, you can export the entire project in one go, which saves a lot of time.

If you create a PDF, then you can merge this PDF file into your master PDF if you intend to have it as one document.

Alternatively, the wireframes can be stored as a separate file and referenced in the main brief document. If you have a large number of wireframes, the export file will be big, so including it separately will be helpful for those that need to access it.

9. Content Outline

The content outline should add some detail to the scope document, such as:

- explaining more about the type of content production,
- who is producing it or if you need someone to do this,
- references to any content style guides you may have, and
- expected production timeframes for the content.

You should also include the Content Master Plan.

That will allow everyone to see the scope of the content requirements and to understand the importance of content in your project.

It won't be considered an afterthought.

The Brief

If your site is going to be ten pages or more, this brief will now include quite a lot of documentation.

Creating an online folder to share with any prospective developers will make good sense. E.g. Dropbox, Google Drive, or similar. In the folder, you can place each of the primary files and the overall guide that makes up the brief.

This way, the summary brief outlined on this page will be the initial document and will reference the other materials.

Once you have compiled all of these documents, you will be ahead of most people preparing for a website development.

You will have built a full blueprint and guide for your web project.

You now have the keys to your success. You won't be leaving the critical decisions up to your developers. You will have provided the design and content teams with a plethora of useful information that allows them to do their job more efficiently.

Not only will you know what your end project will ultimately be like when completed, but it will also be completely purpose-driven. It will be easy to quote and put a project plan to because there won't be any missing pieces or ambiguity.

You can now go to the market and get a fixed price quotation and project plan for this project.

➤ What's Next?

You've have completed the scoping and briefing part of this guide. You now have all the tools to produce your own **Complete Website Planning Guide.**

We also have a Facebook group exclusively for people who have purchased this or the original book. We offer instructions, help and additional information as well as an opportunity to get your questions answered there.

Join the group:

https://www.facebook.com/groups/websiteplan/

We would love to hear from you and learn how this guide has helped you to scope and deliver better web projects. You can follow us on Twitter @ireckon or email us **info@websiteplanningguide.com.**

➤ A Note From Darryl

Thanks for purchasing this workbook and investing time into planning your next web project.

My goal with this series is to help you plan and subsequently create better websites.

As a client you need to get the site built, your stakeholders want the new site developed and performing so for you time is always precious.

As the developer or agency you want to be able to have a smooth project that creates a great result for your client and also is a profitable venture.

Both sides of the table ultimately want the same thing, a great result for the client that produces results.

My challenge to you is to continue to invest the time before each project to create a plan, to challenge each other to ask more questions before the first pixel is designed, before the first line of code is written.

It is the only guaranteed way to create the best results.

This workbook goes deeper into the processes behind the original first book. The steps here are designed to help you create the plan. While it works well on its own, coupled with the original book, you get the complete picture on the process.

Additionally, there are still many great posts online about some of the more detailed steps. No workbook could give enough pages to the depths of research or even charting results. I've provided lots of steps and space for you to do that, but as the owner of this book, you can also join our closed facebook group and ask for help as well.

I would love to get your feedback, either in the form of a review wherever you bought this book from or by connecting with me online.

You can reach me best on twitter (@ireckon) or through our facebook group, via the contacts page on www.websiteplanningguide.com.

There are some more resources planned in this series including accompanying videos and help as well as pocket guides for freelancers and agencies. Sign up to the newsletter on our site to hear more about those.

I'd love to hear how you have used the guide in your projects.

If you have any issues accessing the online templates please reach out, I'm here to help you build better websites.

Darryl King

About The Author

Darryl King is the founder of Ireckon an Australian based Web Design and Development Agency based in Brisbane.

He has been actively involved in the scoping, planning and project management of thousands of web projects.

The Complete Website Planning Guide was born from the frustrations and problems the lack of proper brief documents caused for both his development teams as well as his clients. After searching and trying many different functional specification documents, advertising briefs and other simplistic website planning tools that barely skimmed the surface of what clients need to provide, he developed and tested **The Complete Website Planning Guide**.

Darryl uses the advanced version of this process in his consulting with clients to develop their website scoping documents and plans.

After many requests for additional help in the planning process and based on the success of the first book this workbook was a natural extension to provide more hands-on assistance.

He also conducts workshops, site audits and does speaking events to encourage a more thorough approach to website development.

Acknowledgements

As always special thanks goes to my wife Gill, who never falters in her support of my crazy ideas.

Thanks to all the clients over more than twenty years that have helped in creating this system and provided the knowledge and learnings that make up the content of these books.

Special mention should go to the many team members over the years who pushed me to find a better way to help them do a better job.

Thanks to Lauren Atkinson from Sitting Pretty Graphics who worked tirelessly on the layout of this workbook.

➤ Also By Darryl King

A step-by-step guide for website owners and agencies on how to create a practical and successful scope of works for your next web design project.

The Complete Website Planning Guide will show you how to:

- Get the absolute best out of your website
- Set worthwhile goals
- Understand which audience you serve
- Write a briefing document that will give you more control over the result
- Get better quotes for your site
- Help with project management of your new site

Available in Ebook and Print formats

CPSIA information can be obtained
at www.ICGtesting.com
Printed in the USA
LVHW020235261119
638513LV00003B/20/P